D1162537

PROBABILITY AND STATISTICS
FOR EVERYMAN

Books by Irving Adler

IRVING ADLER

Probability and Statistics for Everyman

How to Understand and Use the Laws of Chance

With diagrams by Ruth Adler

The John Day Company   New York

© 1963 by Irving and Ruth Adler

Library of Congress Catalogue Card Number: 62-16293

Contents

PROBABILITY AND STATISTICS
FOR EVERYMAN

CHAPTER I

A World of Chance

The Accidental Is the Rule

"THE best laid schemes o' mice an' men gang aft agley." In these well-known words Robert Burns reminds us that chance events intrude themselves into our lives at every turn. In all the things we do, whether trivial or significant, accident plays a part. It dogs our steps from life to death. Chance is a factor in the birth of every child. Conception is an accident, and there is a fifty-fifty chance that the child will be a boy or girl. Chance helps us choose our mates, since most marriages grow out of an accidental encounter. Automobile accidents, fires, earthquakes, and floods are grim reminders that chance also has a hand in choosing the time when we will die.

Chance or random events play a part in our industrial activities. A carefully designed machine may turn out perfect products in the main, but now and then, and without warning, it produces a defective product. The random production of defects is undesirable but unavoidable. On the other hand, there are situations in industry where the random character of some events is a desirable feature. The telephone exchange is quite happy to receive calls at random. It becomes jammed when, because of a snowstorm, telephone calls cease to be randomly distributed in time, and nearly all subscribers try to make calls at the same time.

Chance is a characteristic feature of the universe. Although the stars are organized in large assemblages called galaxies, the galaxies are scattered through space at random. Although cosmic rays pour in on the earth from space in a fairly steady stream, and are guided to particular regions of the earth by the earth's magnetic field, they strike particular points of these regions at random. Now and then a cosmic ray makes a direct hit on a gene in a germ cell of a plant or animal, and changes it. In this way the heredity of the plant or animal is changed by accident, and it produces descendants that are somewhat different from its ancestors. Inside a placid-looking drop of water there is a random dance of molecules, visible under the microscope as *Brownian movement*. And the light by which we see all this consists of photons whose small scale movements have a random component, and which are themselves produced by electrons falling at random from higher to lower energy levels in the atom.

We cannot predict with certainty whether a child that is conceived will be a boy or a girl. We cannot predict with certainty whether the next product made by a machine will be perfect or defective. We cannot predict with certainty whether a dust particle, bombarded by molecules in a drop of water, will next move this way or that. Because of the widespread occurrence of chance events, we can predict with certainty that in everything we do or see we shall encounter some things that are unpredictable.

The Accidental Follows Rules

The occurrence of events at random does not imply a complete absence of order. We can be certain about some consequences of uncertainty. While no one knows whether his next child will be a boy or a girl, we can be sure that of all the children born next year about half will be boys and half will be girls. While the telephone company cannot anticipate how many calls will be made in any one minute, it can anticipate what the maximum number of simultaneous calls is likely to be, and can prepare itself to handle that many. While we cannot tell in advance whether a single trial with fair dice will turn up the number seven, we are pretty sure that in many trials the number seven is likely to turn up one sixth of the time. While there is uncertainty associated with the occurrence of single random events, there is some regularity in the distribution of many such events. In the course of repetition, order emerges from chaos. Random occurrences, like fully determined events, are governed by certain rules. It is the business of the theory of probability to discover these rules. Armed with a knowledge of these rules, the mathematician or statistician has the means for making sensible predictions about the unpredictable.

A Realm of Paradox

The goal of the theory of probability is inherently paradoxical: to draw certain conclusions about uncertain events. For this reason you should not be surprised to find paradox lurking in every corner of the subject. As we develop the principal concepts of probability theory and use them to answer some common questions, don't be surprised if we come up with surprising answers. After many such experiences you will learn that in probability theory the unexpected may often be expected.

How the Subject Began

The mathematical theory of probability grew up out of the study of problems arising in games of chance. The Chevalier de Méré, who was fond of gambling, had submitted these problems to the mathematician Pascal. Pascal discussed the problems and his solutions with Fermat in 1654, and thus opened up a new branch of mathematical theory. Many eminent mathematicians have contributed to it since. Today this theory that grew out of the frivolous interests of a French knight is an elaborate scientific structure that has many applications in the physical, biological and social sciences and touches on some of the most profound questions of contemporary philosophy.

One of the problems sent to Pascal by the Chevalier de Méré is known as the *Problem of Points*. Here is a simple version of it: Two gamblers are playing a game that consists of a sequence of trials. (The trial might be, for example tossing a coin.) The outcome of each trial is that one or the other player wins a point. Assume that, at each trial, the players have equal chances of winning the point. It has been agreed that the player who first accumulates three points wins the game. Each player has staked 32 pistoles on the game. If the game is brought to an end before either player has won 3 points, how shall they divide the stakes?

You may want to try your hand at answering this question without any help. Try to answer it now before reading beyond this chapter. Then try again after you have finished reading through Chapter V. Pascal's answer, with his own explanation of his reasoning, is printed in the answer section at the end of the book.

Statistical Probability

In the course of the study of probability questions, two different views of probability have developed. One of them, often referred to as *subjective probability*, interprets probability as a measure of a person's degree of belief in a conclusion based on incomplete evidence. The other view, known as that of *physical* or *statistical probability*, interprets probability as a sort of long-run frequency with which one of many possible outcomes of an experiment occurs when the experiment is repeated many times. The *mathematical theory of probability* is abstracted from the concept of statistical probability. In its present form, like modern algebra and modern geometry, it is based on the theory of sets. The statistical approach to probability is based largely on the work begun during the first quarter of this century by R. A. Fisher and R. von Mises. It was given a foundation in set theory by A. Kolmogoroff in 1933. This volume is chiefly an elementary introduction to the concepts and uses of statistical probability. A possible relationship between the two kinds of probability is discussed in Chapter XII.

CHAPTER II

Sample Spaces and Events

Sample Space

A SIMPLE experiment that results in chance events is that of rolling a die. When the die comes to rest, one of the numbers 1, 2, 3, 4, 5 or 6 is on the top face. If we ask the question, "Which number came out on top?" there are six possible answers. Each of these possible answers is a possible outcome of the experiment. The set of numbers {1, 2, 3, 4, 5, 6} each of which designates one of these possible outcomes, is called a *sample space* for the experiment.

Instead of asking, "Which number came out on top?" we might ask, "Is the number that comes out on top odd or even?" There are two possible answers to this question. Then, with respect to this question, there are two possible outcomes. The set of words, {odd, even}, designating these two possible outcomes, is also a sample space for the experiment of rolling a single die. If we ask the question, "Is the number that comes out on top an ace?", then, with respect to this question, we obtain a third sample space, {ace, not an ace}, for the same experiment.

It is not necessary to roll a real die to discover the possible outcomes of rolling one. We can itemize the possible outcomes (in relation to some specific question we have in mind) by simply imagining that a die has been rolled. In that case the experiment is a purely conceptual one. These considerations lead us to the following definition: *A sample space for a real or conceptual experiment is a set of symbols designating possible outcomes of the experiment,* where each possible outcome is a possible answer to some specific question, and where the result of any performance of the experiment corresponds to one and only one member of the set.

The example of rolling a die shows that there may be more than one sample space for an experiment. Which sample space we choose will depend, in part, on what question we have in mind when we perform the experiment. However, another consideration may influence our choice, too. Suppose, for example, we choose as sample space for the experiment of rolling a die the set {odd, even}. That would mean that each time the die is rolled we record whether the number that comes out on top is odd or even. Then suppose we decide to ask, "What number came out on top in each roll?". Our record will not be able to supply the answer. On the other hand, if we use as sample space the set {1, 2, 3, 4, 5, 6}, we record the actual number that comes out on top in each roll. This record will also supply the answer to the question, "Is the number odd or even?". So the sample space, {1, 2, 3, 4, 5, 6} has an advantage over the sample space {odd, even} for this experiment. It permits us to answer more questions about the experiment. The finer the classification of possible outcomes in a sample space, the more useful that sample space will be. When we study probability questions about the outcomes of an experiment, we shall choose a sample space that provides a classification which is fine enough to permit us to answer all the questions we intend to ask.

Not every listing of possible outcomes of an experiment constitutes a sample space. For example, the set {1, 2, 3, 4, 5} is not a sample space for the experiment of rolling a die, because although 6 is a possible outcome of the experiment, it does not correspond to any member of the set. The set {odd, even, ace} is not a sample space for the experiment because the outcome 1 corresponds to two members of the set, namely, *odd* and *ace*.

When we toss a coin, the coin may land with *head* on top, or with *tail* on top. It may also land in such a manner that the coin stands up on end or leans against some object. In these cases we do not count the toss, and toss the coin again. So, for the experiment of tossing a coin there are only two possible outcomes. If we use H to stand for head, and T to stand for tail, the set $\{H, T\}$ is a sample space for the experiment.

If we toss a coin repeatedly until *head* comes up for the first time, the *head* may turn up on the first toss, or the second toss, or the third toss, and so on. We may designate these possible outcomes by H, TH, TTH, and so on. It is also possible that *head* never turns up at all. We can represent the latter possibility by TTT . . . , where the three dots indicate that the *tails* are repeated in an endless sequence. A suitable sample space for this experiment is the set $\{TTT$ . . . , $H, TH, TTH, . . .\}$, where the last 3 dots signify that the sequence of members of the set continues endlessly. This example shows that some experiments have an infinite sample space. However, nearly all the sample spaces we shall use in this book are finite sample spaces. Whenever the term "sample space" is used in what follows, assume that it is a finite sample space unless it is explicitly identified as an infinite one.

Events in a Sample Space

Let us return now to the experiment of rolling a single die. Choose as sample space the set $\{1, 2, 3, 4, 5, 6\}$, and designate this set by the capital letter S, so we may write $S = \{1, 2, 3, 4, 5, 6\}$. Let us roll the die, and watch for the event, "The number that turns up is even." This event will occur if either the number 2, or 4, or 6 turns up. The event occurs, then, if the outcome of the experiment is a member of the set $E_1 = \{2, 4, 6\}$, where E_1 is simply a name we have assigned to the set for convenience in talking about it. The set E_1 is a subset of the set S, that is, all the members of E_1 belong to S.

Suppose, now, we watch for the event, "The number

that turns up is divisible by 3." This event occurs if the outcome of the experiment is a member of the set $E_2 = \{3, 6\}$, which is also a subset of S. If the event we are watching for is "The number that turns up is a perfect square," this event occurs if the outcome of the experiment is a member of the set $E_3 = \{1, 4\}$. If we watch for the event "The number that turns up is prime," it occurs when the outcome of the experiment is a member of the set $E_4 = \{2, 3, 5\}$. Every possible event that may occur when the experiment is performed leads in the same way to a subset of S. Moreover, if we choose arbitrarily any subset of S, say, $E_5 = \{1, 3, 4\}$, we may, if we wish, watch for the event, "The number 1, 3, or 4 turns up." These observations lead us to make the following definition: An event in a sample space for an experiment is a subset of that space. We say the event *occurs* when the outcome of the experiment is a member of that subset.

To clarify the full meaning of this definition it is necessary to explain the meaning we shall attach to the word *subset*. From what has been said above, it is obvious that we intend to consider as a subset of S any set whose members belong to S. A set that contains some of the members of S and has no members that are not in S clearly qualifies as a subset of S. Moreover, the set S itself also qualifies, because its members are members of S. An event in a sample space may contain *all* or *some* of the members of the space.

The Certain Event

There is obviously something special about the event S which contains all the members of the sample space S. If we perform the experiment of rolling a die, and repeat it many times, the event E_1 occurs only sometimes. It does not occur any time that the number that turns up is odd. On the other hand, the event S always occurs, because all possible outcomes belong to S. For this reason we shall call S the *certain event* in the sample space S, that is, the event that is certain to occur every time the experiment is performed.

The Impossible Event

Suppose we take the set S and gradually remove its members, one at a time. After the last member has been removed, no members are left in the set. You may be tempted to say then that there is no set left. However, we shall find it useful to agree to say that there is a set left that has no members. To visualize it, think of a pair of braces, like those we have already used to enclose the members of a set, but now with no members shown between the braces: { }. We shall call this set the empty set, and designate it by the symbol $\emptyset$. We shall consider the empty set to be a subset of the sample space S in accordance with the following definition: A subset of S is any set that contains all, some, or none of the members of S, and all of whose members, if there are any, belong to S.

The usefulness of the empty set becomes evident when we try to answer this question: Which subset of S corresponds to the event, "The number that turns up when you roll a die is both a perfect square and a prime." This event occurs when and only when the number that turns up is a member of both E_3 and E_4. An examination of the memberships of these subsets of S shows that there is no member of S that belongs to both of them. In other words, the set of members of S that belong to both E_3 and E_4 is the empty set. This is equivalent to saying that the event is impossible. The division of labor among the subsets of S may be described as follows: When you roll a die, every possible event corresponds to a non-empty subset of S. Every impossible event corresponds to the empty set. For this reason we shall sometimes call the empty set the *impossible event*.

Simple Events

Among the subsets of S there are some that contain only one member. Here is a complete list of these one-member subsets: $E_6 = \{1\}$, $E_7 = \{2\}$, $E_8 = \{3\}$, $E_9 = \{4\}$, $E_{10} = \{5\}$, $E_{11} = \{6\}$. The one-member events play an important part in the theory because we can obtain all "possible" events by uniting an appropriate selection of them. For example, to obtain E_3, unite E_6 and E_9. To obtain E_4, unite E_7, E_8, and E_{10}. Because of their importance, we give them a special name. Any event that contains only one member of a sample space is called a *simple event* in that space.

Sets and Subsets

Since a sample space is a set (of possible outcomes of an experiment), and events are subsets of that set, we shall find it useful to borrow some concepts, notation, and results from the mathematical theory of sets. It is clear from the way in which we have already used the word "set" that a set is merely a collection or assemblage of objects, real or conceptual. The members of a set are called its *elements*. To specify a finite set, we may use a pair of braces as a kind of container for its elements, and put the elements on display between the braces. Or we may define it by merely stating a rule by means of which its elements may be identified. For example, to specify a set S whose entire membership consists of the numbers 1, 2, 3, 4, 5, and 6 we may write $S = \{1, 2, 3, 4, 5, 6\}$. Or we may say that S is the set of integers that are greater than 0 but less than 7. Two sets are considered equal if and only if they contain the same elements.

We have already defined the term *subset*, and introduced the notion of the empty set. The empty set is understood to be a subset of every set. We use the symbol $\subset$ to designate the relation "is a subset of." If F is a subset of E, we write $F \subset E$. We list below three sets containing no elements, one element, and two elements respectively:

$$\varnothing = \{ \ \} \qquad R = \{a\} \qquad T = \{x, y\}$$

The set $\varnothing$ has only one subset: $\varnothing$. The set R has two subsets: $\varnothing$ and R. The set T has four subsets: $\varnothing$, $\{x\}$, $\{y\}$, and T.

For the experiment of rolling a die, let us use as sample space the set $S = \{1, 2, 3, 4, 5, 6\}$, and consider the events $E_3 = \{1, 4\}$ and $E_5 = \{1, 3, 4\}$. Notice that E_3 is a subset of E_5. If the outcome of rolling a die is in E_3, then it is also in E_5. So whenever the event E_3 occurs, the event E_5 also occurs. This fact is sometimes expressed by saying that the event E_3 *implies* the event E_5. Consequently we may read the statement $E_3 \subset E_5$ in two ways. We may use the bare language of set theory, and say E_3 is a subset of E_5. Or we may use the more suggestive language of probability theory, and say E_3 implies E_5.

There is a simple way of picturing the relationships among the subsets of a sample space by means of diagrams known as Venn diagrams. The sample space is represented by the points within a rectangle. A subset of the sample space is represented by a subset of the points within the rectangle. In the diagram below, if the rectangle represents a sample space S, the shaded discs E and F represent events in S, and F is a subset of E.

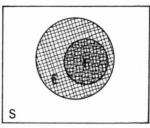

The sample space $F \subset E \subset S$

The Union of Two Sets

When a die is rolled, we say that the vent E_1 *or* E_3 occurs (the number that turns up is even *or* a perfect square) if either of three conditions is satisfied: 1) the number is even, but not a perfect square, so that the outcome is in E_1 but not in E_3; 2) the number is a perfect square, but is not even, so that the outcome is in E_3 but not in E_1; 3) the number is even and a perfect square, so that the outcome is in both E_1 and E_3. Then the event E_1 *or* E_3 is the set $\{1, 2, 4, 6\}$ which unites all the elements that are in E_1 or E_3 or both. In the theory of sets it is called the *union* of E_1 and E_3 and is designated by $E_1 \cup E_3$. (Read this as E_1 *union* E_3.) *If E and F are any two sets in a sample space, $E \cup F$ is the set that contains all those elements and only those elements that are in E or F or both.* The operation of forming the union of two sets is shown in the Venn diagram below.

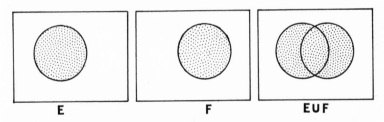

It is clear from the definition of *union*, and from the Venn diagram for the operation, that it makes no difference which of the two sets that are united is placed first. That is, $E \cup F = F \cup E$. In other words, the operation *union* obeys a commutative law that is analogous to the commutative law of addition in arithmetic, where $x + y = y + x$.

To unite three sets E, F, and G, we proceed step by step. First unite E and F to form $E \cup F$. Then unite $E \cup F$ with G. The result is designated by $(E \cup F) \cup G$. We may also first unite F and G to form $F \cup G$, and then unite E with $F \cup G$. The result in this case is designated by $E \cup (F \cup G)$. It is easy to see from a Venn diagram that $(E \cup F) \cup G = E \cup (F \cup G)$. In other words, the operation *union* obeys an associative law analogous to the associative law of addition in arithmetic, where $(x + y) + z = x + (y + z)$. Because of the associative law, we may drop the parentheses and simply write $E \cup F \cup G$ for the set obtained by uniting E, F, and G. By applying both the commutative law and the associative law, we find that $E \cup G \cup F$, $F \cup G \cup E$, etc., obtained by interchanging E, F, and G, are equally good ways of designating the same united set. A similar result is easily obtained even when the number of sets is more than three: When two or more sets are united, it makes no difference in what order the sets are united.

The Intersection of Two Sets

When a die is rolled, let us define E_1 and E_3 as we did on page 18. E_1 occurs when the number that turns up is even. E_3 occurs when the number is a perfect square. We say that the event E_1 *and* E_3 occurs if the number that turns up is even *and* a perfect square. Then the event "E_1 and E_3" is the set $\{4\}$ which contains all the elements that are in both E_1 and E_3. In the theory of sets it is called the intersection of E_1 and E_3 and is designated by $E_1 \cap E_3$. (Read this as E_1 *intersection* E_3.) *If E and F are any two sets in a sample space, $E \cap F$ is the set that contains all the elements and only those elements that are common to both sets.* The operation of forming the intersection of two sets is shown in the diagram on page 25. This operation also obeys a commutative law and an associative law. That is, $E \cap F = F \cap E$, and $(E \cap F) \cap G = E \cap (F \cap G)$. The definition of intersection may be extended to apply to more than two sets: The intersection of any number of sets is the set of all those elements that belong to all

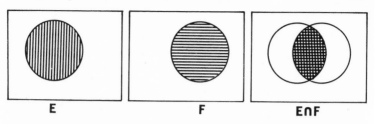

of them. When three or more sets are intersected, they may be intersected successively in any order.

If $E = \{1, 2\}$, $F = \{3, 4\}$, and $G = \{1, 3\}$, then $E \cap G = \{1\}$, $F \cap G = \{3\}$, and $E \cap F =$ the empty set. If the intersection of two sets is the empty set, we say the sets are *disjoint* or *mutually exclusive*. In this case, E and F are disjoint. In a Venn diagram, disjoint sets may be represented by two circles that do not overlap at all.

The Complement of a Set

When a die is rolled, we say the event $E_1 = \{2, 4, 6\}$ does *not* occur if any number except 2, 4 or 6 turns up. The event *not E_1* is the set $\{1, 3, 5\}$ which contains all the elements of the sample space S that are not in E_1. In the theory of sets it is called the *complement* of E_1, and is designated by E'_1. *If E is any set in a sample space S, E' is the set that consists of the elements of S that are not in E.* E is obviously the complement of E', so that $(E')' = E$. A look at the Venn diagram below shows immediately that $E \cup E' = S$, and $E \cap E' = \varnothing$.

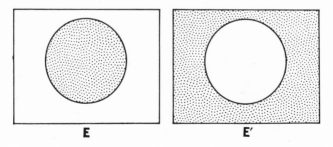

If E, F and G are events in a sample space S, the following relationships are easily verified by means of Venn diagrams: $E \cup \varnothing = E$; $E \cup S = S$; $E \cap S = E$; $E \cap \varnothing = \varnothing$; $E \cup E = E$; $E \cap E = E$; $(E \cup F)' = E' \cap F'$, (the complement of a union is the intersection of the complements); $(E \cap F)' = E' \cup F'$, (the complement of an intersection is the union of the complements); $E \cup (F \cap G) = (E \cup F) \cap (E \cup G)$; and $E \cap (F \cup G) = (E \cap F) \cup (E \cap G)$. The last two relationships are analogous to the distributive law in arithmetic, where $x(y + z) = xy + xz$.

The Number of Elements in a Set

When we calculate the probability of an event we shall sometimes have to count the number of elements in the event. The number of elements in a set E is designated by the symbol $n(E)$. If E and F are events in a sample space S, we can compute the number of elements in $E \cup F$ from $n(E)$ and $n(F)$. The set $E \cup F$ may be thought of as the union of three sets: the set of elements in E but not in F, the set of elements in F but not in E, and the set of elements in both E and F. Using set theory notation, these three sets are $E \cap F'$, $F \cap E'$, and $E \cap F$ respectively. The Venn diagram shows that $n(E)$ is the number of elements in $E \cap F'$ plus the number of elements in $E \cap F$. Also, $n(F)$ is the number of elements in $E \cap F$ plus the number of elements in $F \cap E'$. If we add $n(E)$ and $n(F)$, we are counting the elements of $E \cap F'$ and of $F \cap E'$ once, but we are counting the elements of $E \cap F$ twice. To eliminate this duplication, subtract $n(E \cap F)$. This leads to the formula, $n(E \cup F) = n(E) + n(F) - n(E \cap F)$. In the special case where E and F are disjoint, $n(E \cap F) = 0$, and the formula reduces to $n(E \cup F) = n(E) + n(F)$. In particular, $n(E) + n(E') = n(S)$, since E and E' are disjoint, and their union is the entire sample space S.

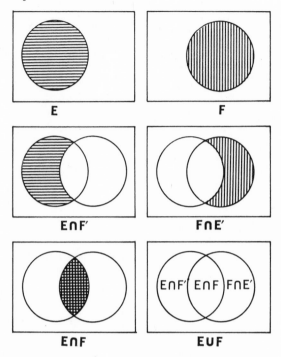

The Product of Sample Spaces

If we perform the experiment of rolling a die, we may use as sample space $S = \{1, 2, 3, 4, 5, 6\}$. If we toss a coin, we may use as sample space $R = \{H, T\}$. If we perform the experiment of first rolling a die and then tossing a coin, the possible outcomes are $(1, H)$, $(2, H)$, $(3, H)$, $(4, H)$, $(5, H)$, $(6, H)$, $(1, T)$, $(2, T)$, $(3, T)$, $(4, T)$, $(5, T)$, and $(6, T)$, where the number, written first, shows how the die turned up, and the letter, written second, shows how the coin turned up. A symbol like $(1, H)$ is known in mathematics as an *ordered pair*. Then a sample space for the compound experiment of rolling a die and tossing a coin is the set of all ordered pairs whose first member is an element of S and whose second member is an element of R. In the theory of sets this set is called the *Cartesian product* of S and R and is designated by $S \times R$.

To obtain the Cartesian product of a set without overlooking any of its elements, it is helpful to draw a tree diagram. From a single starting point draw a line for each element of the set that is supplying the first member of each ordered pair. Then from the free end of each line draw a set of lines, one for each element of the set that is supplying the second member of each ordered pair. Then the diagram looks like branches of a tree, with twigs on each branch. Each path from the starting point to a free end goes first along a branch and then along a twig. The corresponding ordered pair is a member of the product set. The set of all paths corresponds to the entire product set.

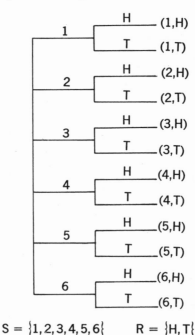

$$S = \{1, 2, 3, 4, 5, 6\} \qquad R = \{H, T\}$$
Tree diagram for S × R

The tree diagram for rolling a die and tossing a coin is shown on page 28.

Inspection of the tree diagram suggests a rule for calculating the number of elements in the product set $S \times R$. All we have to do is multiply the number of elements in S by the number of elements in R. Symbolically we write: $n(S \times R) = n(S) \cdot n(R)$. This rule may also be stated in these words: If a compound experiment consists of first performing one experiment that has n_1 possible outcomes, and then performing a second experiment that has n_2 possible outcomes, then the compound experiment has $n_1 n_2$ possible outcomes.

Tossing Two Coins

If two coins are tossed, either in succession or simultaneously, the possible outcomes for each coin are represented by the sample space $R = \{H, T\}$. A sample space for the experiment of tossing both coins is $R \times R$. To save space, we shall write HT for (H, T), etc. Then $R \times R = \{HH, HT, TH, TT\}$. The number of elements in this set is $n(R)n(R) = 2 \times 2 = 4$.

Rolling Two Dice

If two dice are rolled, either in succession or simultaneously, the possible outcomes for each die are represented by the sample space $S = \{1, 2, 3, 4, 5, 6\}$. A sample space for the experiment of rolling both dice is $S \times S$. The number of elements in $S \times S$ is $n(S)n(S) = 6 \times 6 = 36$.

Tossing Three Coins

If three coins are tossed, we specify a possible outcome by listing in order the outcome for the first coin, the outcome for the second coin, and the outcome for the third coin. For example, HHH, HTH, THT, and so on, are among the possible outcomes. These outcomes are ordered triples in which the first member is an element of the sample space for the experiment of tossing the first coin, the second member is an element of the sample space for the experiment of tossing the second coin, and the third member is an element of the sample space for the experiment of tossing the third coin. The set of all such ordered triples is the Cartesian product of the three sample spaces. In this case, since all three experiments have the same sample space R, the sample space of the compound experiment is $R \times R \times R$. A tree diagram for this Cartesian product is shown below. The same sample space will do if we toss three coins simultaneously or in succession, or if we toss one coin three times.

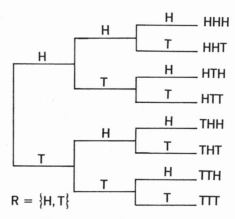

Tree diagram for R × R × R

The concept of Cartesian product is easily extended to define the product of any finite number of sets: If S_1, $S_2, \ldots, S_r$ are r sets, then $S_1 \times S_2 \times \ldots \times S_r$ is the set of all r-tuples $(a_1, a_2, \ldots, a_r)$, where a_1 is an element of S_1, a_2 is an element of S_2, and so on. A tree diagram can always be drawn for the product set. It is easy to see from such a diagram that the number of elements in the product set is given by the rule:

$$n(S_1 \times S_2 \times \ldots \times S_r) = n(S_1)n(S_2) \ldots n(S_r).$$

This is the well-known general *multiplication rule*, which may be expressed in these words: If a compound experiment consists of a sequence of r experiments, and the numbers of possible outcomes of these separate experiments are $n_1, n_2, \ldots, n_r$ respectively, then the number of possible outcomes of the compound experiment is $n_1 \times n_2 \times \ldots \times n_r$.

Exercises for Chapter II

1. If $S = \{a, b, c\}$ is a sample space, list all the events in S (subsets of S). Which of these are simple events? Which is the certain event? Which is the impossible event?
2. If $T = \{x, y, z, w\}$, list all the subsets of T.
3. On page 22 we found that a set with 0 elements has 1 subset, a set with 1 element has 2 subsets, and a set with 2 elements has 4 subsets. How many subsets does a set with 3 elements have? How many subsets does a set with 4 elements have? How many subsets do you think a set with r elements has?
4. If $E = \{0, 1, 2\}$, and $F = \{1, 2, 3, 4\}$, construct the sets $E \cup F$ and $E \cap F$.
5. If $S = \{1, 2, 3, 4, 5, 6\}$, and $E = \{3, 6\}$, what is E'?
6. Draw two identical Venn diagrams showing two events E and F that overlap. In one of the diagrams shade $E \cup F$ with black pencil. Then shade $(E \cup F)'$ with red pencil. In the other diagram shade E' with horizontal lines, and shade F' with vertical lines. Then fill in $E' \cap F'$ with red pencil. Compare the two diagrams to verify that $(E \cup F)' = E' \cap F'$.
7. Draw a tree diagram for $R \times R$, where $R = \{H, T\}$.
8. Draw a tree diagram for $S \times S$, where $S = \{1, 2, 3, 4, 5, 6\}$. Then list all the elements of $S \times S$.

9. Construct a sample space for the experiment of tossing four coins.

10. If S_1, S_2, S_3, S_4, S_5, and S_6 are identical sample spaces, all equal to $\{H, T\}$, how many elements are there in $S_1 \times S_2 \times S_3 \times S_4 \times S_5 \times S_6$?

CHAPTER III

Probability Models

Fair Rolling of a Fair Die

LET us consider the experiment of rolling a single die. Choose as sample space the set $S = \{1, 2, 3, 4, 5, 6\}$. What is the probability that the number 2 will turn up when the die is rolled? The answer commonly given to this question says: All the six numbers are equally likely to turn up, so the probability or chance is 1 out of 6, or $\frac{1}{6}$. To find out what this answer means, let us try to retrace the steps in the reasoning by which it is obtained.

Observation of Repeated Trials. To find out the chance that a 2 will turn up, we might be tempted at first to try to find it empirically by performing an experiment in which we roll the die many times. A little thought, however, shows that repeated trials will not give us an easy answer to the question. Precisely because chance is involved, the frequency with which 2 turns up will vary from experiment to experiment. If, in each experiment, we roll the die six times, in some experiments the 2 will not turn up at all, in some it will turn up 1 time out of 6, in others 2 times out of 6, or 3 times out of 6, and so on. One of these results may occur more often than others, and the frequency with which these results occur in many repetitions of the experiment of rolling a die six times does provide a clue to what the probability of getting a 2 really is. But interpreting this clue is an advanced problem in statistical inference that requires a prior knowledge of the theory of proba-

33

bility. Then this, obviously, is not the path by which people arrive at the commonly accepted answer that the probability that 2 will turn up is $\frac{1}{6}$.

The Symmetry Argument. Since we cannot get the answer easily by actually rolling the die in an experiment, we try next to get it by making some general observations about the nature of the die and the way in which it is rolled. The die is pretty nearly a cube, which is a symmetrical solid. If the die is made of only one substance, and if its weight is uniformly distributed, the die is symmetrical with regard to its physical as well as its geometric properties. In the case of a loaded die the weight is not uniformly distributed, but is concentrated near one of the six faces. Then the die tends to come to rest on this face and turn up the opposite face. Thus the die favors turning up one particular face, and the six possible outcomes are not equally likely. This is obviously not the case we have in mind, so we exclude it by assuming that we are dealing only with a fair die. But even when throwing a fair die, it is possible to favor one particular face by holding that face up, not really shaking the die before throwing it, and then throwing it so that it slides rather than rolls. This is obviously not the kind of throw we have in mind, so we exclude it by specifying that a fair method of rolling the die be used. There still remains the problem of determining whether an actual die is fair, and whether the method of rolling it is fair. We say the die and the method of rolling it are fair if there are equal chances for each of the six faces to turn up, so that each has a probability of $\frac{1}{6}$. And now we find ourselves caught in the act of circular reasoning. We set out to prove that all six numbers have equal chances of turning up, and we ended up by assuming it when we assumed that the die and the method of rolling it are fair. This means, of course, that we have proved nothing.

The Method of Abstraction. To avoid circular reasoning, we give up any attempt at this point to draw conclusions about any particular real die. Instead, we begin frankly with an abstraction, the idealized fair die thrown in a fair way, for which we assume that there are equal chances for the six possible outcomes, so that the probability of each outcome is, *by assumption*, $\frac{1}{6}$. In other words, we do not begin our mathematical theory of the die with a real experiment performed with a real die. We begin it with a purely conceptual experiment with an imaginary die. In fact, we can even dispense with the "experiment," and simply begin with the sample space S, and attach to each of its simple events the number $\frac{1}{6}$, and call this number the probability of the simple event. However, we shall continue to talk about the conceptual experiment underlying the sample space because, as a kind of intuitive diagram for the sample space, it makes it easier for us to understand it, and it also suggest ways in which we can apply the results of our theory.

We can now grasp more clearly the meaning of the statement that all six numbers on a die are equally likely to turn up, so that the probability of each number is $\frac{1}{6}$. It is not a statement about a real experiment with a real die. It is a statement about an abstract *probability model*, and merely specifies the assumptions by which this particular model is defined.

Model for Rolling a Die

In order for the model to be useful, it must include the notion of the probability of any event in the sample space. We have already specified the probability of a simple event by assuming that it is $\frac{1}{6}$. We now *define* the probability of other events in the sample space S as follows: 1) The probability of the empty set is 0. 2) If an event contains more than one element of S, the probability of the event is the sum of the probabilities of the simple events of which it is the union. By this definition, the probability of E_1, (getting an even number), is $\frac{3}{6}$ or $\frac{1}{2}$, the probability of E_3, (getting a perfect square), is $\frac{2}{6}$ or $\frac{1}{3}$, and the probability of S is 1.

It is not necessary for us to use S as a sample space in order to construct a probability model for rolling a die. We may, if we wish, use as a sample space the set $T = \{\text{ace, even, odd prime}\}$, in which the events $\{1\}$, $\{2, 4, 6\}$ and $\{3, 5\}$ of the sample space S are now being used as elements of T. But then we would specify the following probabilities for the elements of T: ace, $\frac{1}{6}$; even, $\frac{1}{2}$; odd prime, $\frac{1}{3}$. This example emphasizes for us a very important fact: *It is not necessary that the probabilities assigned to the elements of a sample space be equal.*

Notice however, that whether we use S or T as sample space, the probability assigned to each element of the sample space is a non-negative number, and the sum of the probabilities of all the elements in each space is 1. We shall incorporate these properties into our general definition of a probability model. *A probability model is a sample space with an assignment of probabilities to the events of the sample space according to this scheme:*

1. *The probability of each simple event is a non-negative number.*
2. *The sum of the probabilities of all the simple events is 1.*
3. *The probability of an event that is not empty is the sum of the probabilities of the simple events that must be united to get that event.*
4. *The probability of the empty set is 0.*

A number is non-negative if it is 0 or a positive number. The wording of condition 1 permits us to assign 0 as the probability of a simple event, if we wish. We shall have occasion to do so in Chapter VII.

To construct a probability model on a sample space, it suffices to assign probabilities to the simple events so that conditions 1) and 2) are satisfied. Then the probabilities of other events are automatically assigned by conditions 3) and 4).

The Uses of a Mathematical Model

It may come as a surprise to some readers that the mathematical theory of probability studies abstract probability models and not real life situations in which chance events occur. However, this is not an unusual procedure. As a matter of fact, it is the characteristic procedure in mathematics. Pure mathematics never studies reality. It studies only abstract models of reality. In geometry, for example, we study the relations among points and lines that have no breadth, although no line drawn with a pencil has this property. In mechanics we study the relations among point-masses, (a point-mass is a mass that is assumed to be concentrated at a single point), although no known mass is a point-mass. This procedure has the following advantages for both theory and practice:

1) The model is clearly defined by an explicit formulation of the assumptions which characterize it.

2) The way is left open for the construction of different models by simply using different assumptions for them. For example, by using three different sets of assumptions in geometry, we get the three models known as euclidean, hyperbolic and elliptic geometry. By using different assumptions in mechanics, we get either Newtonian mechanics, or relativity mechanics.

3) In each mathematical model, since all extraneous factors have been excluded, we can trace with certainty the logical consequences of the assumptions that we have made.

4) We can apply to a real life situation any model whose assumptions correspond approximately to reality. Then the logical consequences of these assumptions become pre-

dictions of what we may expect in the real life situation. When this is done, we pass via applied mathematics from the realm of pure mathematics into the realm of natural science. For example, the assumption that the mass of a body is concentrated at a point is approximately true in astronomy, because the bodies studied there are so small compared to the distances between them. Applying the assumptions of Newtonian mechanics to the solar system, we can predict with considerable accuracy the motions of the planets.

5) We can test how closely a particular mathematical model fits the situation to which it is applied. The result of the test may indicate that a better model is needed. For example, while Newtonian mechanics was generally successful as a model of the solar system, it failed to predict accurately the motion of the planet Mercury. This indicated the need for a better model. Relativity mechanics is that better model.

We shall enjoy the benefits of these five advantages when we construct probability models and then apply them to practical situations.

Some Simple Probability Models

If you open any book on probability theory, you will find the author discussing such things as tossing coins, rolling dice, drawing cards from a deck, drawing balls from urns, and placing objects into cells. This does not mean that the book is designed as a handbook for gamblers, although it may serve that purpose. The games of chance are studied in idealized form as probability models which may be applied to the study of important practical problems. We construct below some of these models, and give examples of situations to which they may be applied.

Tossing a Coin. The sample space for a single toss of the coin is the set $\{H, T\}$. Assume that the two possible outcomes are equally likely. Then the probability of each of the simple events $\{H\}$ and $\{T\}$ is $\frac{1}{2}$. This is the model that is usually referred to as "tossing a fair coin."

If E is an event, and its probability is q, we write $P(E) = q$. Using this notation, we may write the assumptions for this model as follows: $P(\{H\}) = \frac{1}{2}$, $P(\{T\}) = \frac{1}{2}$.

An important use of the fair coin model occurs in the Mendelian theory of heredity. The theory is used to explain the transmission of certain traits from parents to offspring. We give a brief sketch of the theory as applied to the crossing of red-flowered and white-flowered peas. It is assumed that the color of the flower is determined by a *gene*, and that this gene may occur in one of two forms, a gene for redness, denoted by C, and a gene for whiteness, denoted by c. Each plant has a pair of such genes. The pair may be CC or Cc or cc. A plant that contains the pair CC has red flowers. A plant that contains the pair cc has white flowers. A plant that has the pair Cc is a hybrid, as far as its genetic makeup is concerned, but its flowers are red nevertheless. Since the gene C imposes its effects even in the presence of the gene c, C is called *dominant*.

The pea flower reproduces sexually through the formation of male and female germ cells (pollen grains and egg cells). A pollen grain and an egg cell fuse to form a seed, which is the beginning of a new plant. When a germ cell is formed, it receives from its parent just one of the two flower-color genes that the parent has. If the parent is a hybrid, with the gene pair Cc, each germ cell receives either C or c as part of its hereditary makeup. The two outcomes are assumed to be equally likely, so that the transmission of color genes by a hybrid plant may be described by means of a probability model using the sample space $\{C, c\}$, and probability assignments $P(\{C\}) = \frac{1}{2}$ and $P(\{c\}) = \frac{1}{2}$. This is the same as the fair coin model, except that we have written C instead of H, and c instead of T. We shall pursue this example further when we discuss the model for tossing two coins.

Tossing a Tack. If a tack is tossed into the air, it may land on the ground point *up* or point *down,* as shown in the drawing. Let us use the words *up* and *down* to denote the two possible outcomes. As in the case of tossing a fair coin, we have a two element sample space. But in this case the two outcomes need not be equally likely. If the probability that the tack lands point up is p, (a number between 0

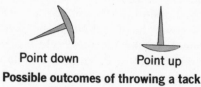

Point down   Point up

Possible outcomes of throwing a tack

and 1), then the probability that the tack lands point down is $1 - p$, since the sum of the two probabilities must be 1. If we use the letter q to denote $1 - p$, this probability model is characterized by the following statements: The sample space is {up, down}. $P(\{up\}) = p$. $P(\{down\}) = q$. $p + q = 1$. If the distribution of weight between the head and the point of the tack is such that $p = q = \frac{1}{2}$, then the model is the same as that of the fair coin, except that we have written *up* instead of H, and *down* instead of T. However, the model is different if p is not equal to $\frac{1}{2}$. We might have, for example, $p = \frac{1}{3}$, $q = \frac{2}{3}$. Or we might have $p = .21$, $q = .79$. Strictly speaking, we have here not one model but an infinite family of models. We get one specific model in the family by specifying a particular value for p. The fair coin model is one of the members of the family.

It seems intuitively obvious that we need one of these two-element models, with $p \neq \frac{1}{2}$ (*read as p not equal to $\frac{1}{2}$*) to describe the experiment of tossing a real thumb-tack. It is less obvious, but undoubtedly true, that we need the same type of model to describe the experiment of tossing a real coin, since a real coin is not perfectly symmetrical, and hence *head* and *tail* are not equally likely outcomes. However, for a real coin, $P(H)$, though not exactly equal to $\frac{1}{2}$, would be very close to it.

Tossing Two Coins, or Tossing One Coin Twice. The sample space for this experiment is $\{HH, HT, TH, TT\}$. If the coins are fair we assume that the four possible outcomes are equally likely, so that $P(\{HH\}) = P(\{HT\}) = P(\{TH\}) = P(\{TT\}) = \frac{1}{4}$. If E is the event that exactly one head turns up, then $E = \{HT, TH\} = \{HT\} \cup \{TH\}$. So $P(E) = P(\{HT\}) + P(\{TH\}) = \frac{1}{4} + \frac{1}{4} = \frac{1}{2}$.

We have already seen that tossing a fair coin can serve as a probability model for the formation of germ cells by a hybrid pea-flower that contains the gene pair Cc. Tossing two coins can serve as a model for the mating of hybrid flowers, since each seed receives two color genes, one from each parent flower, via the germ cells that fuse to form the seed. If, as we did before, we substitute C for H, and c for T, we find that the set of possible outcomes of mating hybrid flowers is $\{CC, Cc, cC, cc\}$, and the probability of each of these four outcomes is $\frac{1}{4}$. Some of the interesting events for the biologist are these: $E_1 =$ the seed is pure-bred red, that is, it contains only genes for redness, so that the flower that grows from it is red; $E_2 =$ the seed is hybrid-red, that is, it contains both genes, and produces a red flower since redness is dominant; $E_3 =$ the seed grows into a red flower, either pure-bred or hybrid; $E_4 =$ the seed is pure-bred white, that is, it contains only genes for whiteness, so that the flower that grows from it is white. Clearly, $E_1 = \{CC\}$, $E_2 = \{Cc, cC\}$, $E_3 = \{CC, Cc, cC\}$, and $E_4 = \{cc\}$. It follows that $P(E_1) = \frac{1}{4}$, $P(E_2) = \frac{1}{2}$, $P(E_3) = \frac{3}{4}$, and $P(E_4) = \frac{1}{4}$. *When hybrid red pea plants are mated, 3 out of 4 of the offspring are likely to be red, and only 1 out of 4 are likely to be white. Of the red offspring, 2 out of 3 are likely to be hybrid, and 1 out of three is likely to be pure-bred.*

Tossing a Coin k Times. Consider first the case of tossing a coin 3 times, so that $k = 3$. The sample space is $\{HHH, HHT, HTH, THH, HTT, THT, TTH, TTT\}$. If the coins are fair, the eight possible outcomes are equally likely, and each simple event is assigned the probability $\frac{1}{8}$. If E is the event that exactly 2 heads turn up, then $E = \{HHT, HTH, THH\}$, $n(E) = 3$, and $P(E) = \frac{3}{8}$.

In the general case of tossing k coins, the sample space of possible outcomes is $S_1 \times S_2 \ldots \times S_k$, where S_1, $S_2, \ldots, S_k$ are all equal to $\{H, T\}$. By the multiplication rule stated on page 31, the number of possible outcomes is $2 \times 2 \times \ldots \times 2$, where 2 appears as a factor k times. This product, as you learned in high school algebra, is written as 2^k. If the coins are fair, the outcomes are assumed to be equally likely, and the probability of each simple event is $\dfrac{1}{2^k}$. Suppose E is the event that exactly r heads (and hence $k - r$ tails) turn up. To find $P(E)$ we must count the number of elements in E. This counting problem will be taken up in the next chapter. Meanwhile, using the notation introduced on page 26, we may denote the number of elements in E by $n(E)$. Then $P(E) = n(E) \left(\dfrac{1}{2^k} \right) = n(E)/2^k$.

Drawing Balls from an Urn. Suppose there are 3 white balls and 5 black balls thoroughly mixed in an urn. If a ball is drawn from the urn *at random*, what is the probability that it is white? What is the probability that it is black? To answer these questions, let us assume that the white balls are numbered from 1 to 3, and the black balls are numbered from 1 to 5, so that balls of the same color are easily distinguished from each other. Since any one of the eight balls may be drawn, we may use as sample space for the experiment the set $S = \{w_1, w_2, w_3, b_1, b_2, b_3, b_4, b_5\}$. Saying that the ball is drawn *at random* is a short way of saying that the eight balls are equally likely to be drawn.

Therefore the probability of each simple event is $\frac{1}{8}$. If we denote by E the event that a white ball is drawn, and by F the event that a black ball is drawn, then $E = \{w_1, w_2, w_3\}$, $F = \{b_1, b_2, b_3, b_4, b_5\}$, $n(E) = 3$, and $n(F) = 5$. $P(E) = \frac{3}{8}$, and $P(F) = \frac{5}{8}$.

Since we are concerned only with the color of the ball that is drawn, we could use instead of the 8-element sample space S a 2-element sample space $T = \{w, b\}$, with $P(\{w\}) = \frac{3}{8}$, and $P(\{b\}) = \frac{5}{8}$. This second model for the urn experiment is like the model for throwing a tack, with w written instead of *up*, and b written instead of *down*.

To make the model more general, suppose the urn contains r white balls and s black balls, so that the total number of balls in the urn is $r + s$. We may use as sample space the set $S = \{w_1, \ldots, w_r, b_1, \ldots, b_s\}$, with the $r + s$ possible outcomes assumed to be equally likely. Then the probability of each simple event is $1/(r + s)$. The probability of drawing a white ball is $r/(r + s)$, and the probability of drawing a black ball is $s/(r + s)$. We may, if we wish, use a 2-element sample space $T = \{w, b\}$, with $P(\{w\}) = r/(r + s)$, and $P(\{b\}) = s/(r + s)$. Again, the latter model is like the model for throwing a tack.

Equally Likely Outcomes. We have seen several specific models for which the sample space consisted of equally likely possible outcomes. We can now set up a general model for all such experiments. If there are n possible outcomes, $a_1, \ldots, a_n$, then the sample space $S = \{a_1, \ldots, a_n\}$, and $n(S) = n$. The probability of each simple event in S is $1/n$, which may also be written as $1/n(S)$. Suppose E is an event that consists of r possible outcomes, that is, $n(E) = r$. Then $P(E) = r(1/n) = r/n$, which may also be written as $n(E)/n(S)$.

In discussions about chance events, it is common practice to talk about the *odds* in favor of the event. This concept is related to the probability of the event by the following definition: Let E be an event in a sample space

S, and let E' be its complement. The odds in favor of E is the ratio $P(E)/P(E')$. If S consists of n equally likely possible outcomes, and E contains r elements, then $P(E) = r/n$, and $P(E') = (n - r)/n$. Then in this case the odds in favor of E will be $r/(n - r)$. For example, if there are 8 possible outcomes in the sample space, and E contains 3 of them while E' contains the other 5, then the odds in favor of E will be $\frac{3}{5}$.

Repeated Drawings with Replacement. Suppose an urn contains r white balls and s black balls. A ball is drawn at random, and is then replaced. The balls in the urn are mixed thoroughly, and another ball is drawn and replaced. This is repeated k times. What is the probability that m of the balls drawn are white? We have already seen that the experiment of drawing one ball is equivalent, as a probability model, to the experiment of throwing a tack. When the ball is replaced, the conditions of the experiment are restored. Then the next drawing is a repetition of the same experiment. So a compound experiment consisting of repeated drawings from the urn with replacement is equivalent as a probability model to repeated tossing of a tack. As stated on page 42, we are postponing further consideration of this model until we solve some counting problems in the next chapter.

The model of repeated tossing of a tack, or repeated drawings, with replacement, from an urn containing balls of two colors, is one that is often used in industry for quality control of a product. Suppose a machine, when properly adjusted, has a small probability, say .01, of turning out a defective product. Then the experiment of turning out one product may be represented by the sample space $S = \{g, d\}$, where g stands for *good* product, d stands for *defective* product, $P(\{g\}) = .99$, and $P(\{d\}) = .01$. Turning out k products is k repetitions of this experiment, and hence is like tossing a tack k times. To check on the performance of the machine, the manufacturer will take a sample of its products and test them for defects. He would like to know how large a sample he needs for an effective, yet inexpensive test. He would also like to know how many defective products he should expect to find in the sample. If he finds too large a number, then he would know that the machine is out of adjustment. These questions can be answered for the manufacturer by analyzing the probability model for repeated tossing of a tack.

In future discussions of repeated experiments we shall modify our terminology a bit in order to avoid confusion. We shall call each repetition a *trial*, and we shall call the whole set of repeated trials the *experiment*. Thus, tossing a coin 3 times will be called an experiment made up of 3 trials.

Drawing without Replacement. Suppose an urn contains r white balls and s black balls, and k balls are drawn at random, without replacement. This is equivalent to making one drawing of k balls. What is the probability that a specified number m of the k balls drawn will be white? To answer this question, we shall have to set up a sample space of equally likely outcomes, and then count those that occur in the event "m balls are white." We postpone further study of this question, too, until we learn some counting techniques in the next chapter.

The experiment of drawing from an urn without replacement is relevant to the quality control problem described above. The set of all products of a machine, both good and defective, is like a set of balls in an urn. Taking a sample of the products for testing is like drawing balls from the urn *without replacement*. However, if the number of products made is very large compared to the number of products in the sample, the necessary calculations may be made as if the drawings had been made *with replacement*. This turns out to simplify the calculations. Although the simplification introduces an error, the error is too small to be significant.

Drawing from an Urn with Numbered Chips. Suppose an urn contains numbered chips, where the number on each chip is one of the numbers $a_1, a_2, \ldots, a_k$. Assume that the number of chips with the number a_1 is n_1, the number of chips with the number a_2 is n_2, and so on. Then the total number of chips $n = n_1 + n_2 + \ldots + n_k$. If a chip is drawn at random from the urn, we may use as sample space $S = \{a_1, a_2, \ldots, a_k\}$, with probabilities assigned to simple events as follows: $P(\{a_1\}) = n_1/n$, $P(\{a_2\}) = n_2/n, \ldots, P(\{a_k\}) = n_k/n$.

A well-known example to which this model applies is that of drawing a card from a shuffled bridge deck. We may think of the numbers as $1, 2, \ldots, 10, 11, 12, 13$, where the last three numbers represent jack, queen and king respectively. Then $n_1 = n_2 = \ldots = n_{13} = 4$. On the other hand, if we are concerned only with the suit of a card, we may think of the cards as bearing the numbers 1, 2, 3, and 4, representing spades, clubs, hearts, and diamonds respectively. Then $n_1 = n_2 = n_3 = n_4 = 13$.

Another example to which the model applies is the male population of the United States classified according to shoe size. Then each man is like a chip in the urn, and his shoe size is the number on the chip. A shoe dealer who has 25 customers in a day would like to know how many calls he is likely to have for each shoe size. This is like asking, When 25 chips are drawn from the urn, "how many of each number are likely to be drawn?" Questions like this one, concerning samples drawn from a population, will be taken up in later chapters. Problems about population samples may be of two main types. In the first type, as in the example just mentioned, we know in advance the probabilities of the different kinds of chips in the population, and we try to predict the properties of samples chosen at random from the population. In the second type, we do not know in advance the probabilities of the different kinds of chips in the population. We draw at random a sample of the population, and then, after observing the properties of the sample, we try to infer what the probabilities of the different kinds of chips in the population are likely to be. Problems of the second type are problems of *statistical inference*. Public opinion polls and market surveys involve exercises of this type.

Urn Model for Contagious Diseases. During outbreaks of a contagious disease, every time a person catches the disease there is an increase in the probability that others will catch it. This kind of situation is represented approximately by an urn model: An urn contains r white balls and s black balls. A ball is drawn at random from the urn, and is replaced. Then t balls of the same color are added to the urn. The process is repeated over and over. The sample space for each trial is $\{w, b\}$. But the probability assigned to each simple event in the space varies from trial to trial and depends on the outcome of the preceding trials. In the first trial, the probability of drawing a white ball is $r/(r + s)$. If the first ball drawn is white, then in the second trial the probability of drawing a white ball is $(r + t)/(r + s + t)$, since the number of white balls and the total number of balls have both been increased by t. This probability is larger than $r/(r + s)$.

Putting Objects into Cells. A mail clerk who is custodian of 3 mail boxes that are side by side has 2 letters to put into these boxes. He is a rather unreliable clerk who pays no attention to the address on a letter but simply picks a box for it at random. Let us construct a sample space for the experiment of putting the 2 letters into the 3 boxes. Before we actually construct the sample space we can predict how many elements it will have by using the multiplication rule stated on page 31. If we denote the two letters by a and b, we may think of the experiment of putting the two letters into the boxes as a compound experiment made up of two steps. The first step is choosing a box for letter a. This may be done in 3 ways. The second step is choosing a box for letter *b*. This may be done in 3 ways. By the multiplication rule, the compound experiment may be done in $3 \times 3 = 9$ ways.

The 9 possible outcomes are shown in the diagram below. If both letters are in one box, that box might be the first, second or third box. These three cases are shown in the first line. If each letter is in a separate box, then two boxes have a letter and the remaining box is empty. The empty box may be the first, second or third box. The second line shows three such cases, with *a* always to the

Possible outcomes when 2 different objects are put into 3 cells (sample space S)

left of *b*. The third line shows three more cases that are obtained from these by interchanging *a* and *b*. The diagram may be taken as the sample space, *S*. The outcomes are assumed to be equally likely, so that the probability of each simple event is $\frac{1}{9}$.

An important feature of an outcome is the number of objects that are found in each cell. In the first outcome shown on the first line of the diagram, for example, the three cells contain 2, 0, 0 objects respectively. The numbers 2, 0, 0 are called the *occupancy numbers* of the outcome. The other two outcomes on the first line have occupancy numbers 0, 2, 0 and 0, 0, 2 respectively. The outcomes shown on the second line have occupancy numbers 0, 1, 1 and 1, 0, 1 and 1, 1, 0 respectively. The outcomes shown on the third line have the same occupancy numbers as those above them in the second line.

Suppose now that instead of two letters the clerk has

two identical printed circulars to put into the boxes. To show that the circulars are identical, denote them both by ∗. Then the 9 possible outcomes, with a and b replaced by ∗ look like this:

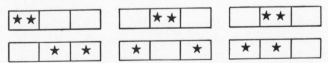

Possible outcomes when 2 objects that look alike are put into 3 cells

Notice that each outcome on the second line is indistinguishable in appearance, from the one shown under it on the third line. This is a result of the fact that they have the same occupancy numbers. We must show the two indistinguishable outcomes separately because, although they look alike, they are arrived at in different but equally likely ways. This becomes apparent if we imagine that the clerk had written a on the back of one of the circulars and b on the back of the other circular before putting them into the boxes. Then each outcome on the second line is indistinguishable from the outcome shown under it if you look only at the front of each circular, but the two outcomes are distinguishable if you also look at the back.

If the circulars are considered indistinguishable, it is natural to use a smaller sample space T as follows, obtained from the list of 9 possible outcomes shown above by omitting the third line:

Possible distinguishable outcomes when 2 objects that look alike are put into 3 cells (sample space T)

However, under our assumption that the clerk picks a box at random for each circular, each outcome shown on the first line can be obtained in only one of the nine equally likely ways of putting the circulars into the boxes, while each outcome on the second line can be obtained in two ways. That is, each element on the first line corresponds to one element of S, but each element on the second line corresponds to two elements of S. Hence we must assign a probability of $\frac{1}{9}$ to each simple event that contains an outcome shown on the first line, and a probability of $\frac{2}{9}$ to each simple event that contains an outcome shown on the second line. If we represent each box by the space between adjacent vertical bars, we can write down the assignment of probabilities in this way: $P(\{| ** | | |\}) = \frac{1}{9}$, $P(\{| | ** | |\}) = \frac{1}{9}$, $P(\{| | | ** |\}) = \frac{1}{9}$, $P(\{| | * | * |\}) = \frac{2}{9}$, $P(\{| * | | * |\}) = \frac{2}{9}$, $P(\{| * | * | |\}) = \frac{2}{9}$. Let us call the probability model obtained in this way *cell model I*. We note for future reference that the sample space T used in this model consists of all the distinguishable outcomes obtained when 2 objects that look alike are placed in 3 cells, and that in this model the possible outcomes are not equally likely.

To get a generalized version of cell model I, we would first consider the problem of putting r different objects into n cells. If we assume that a cell is chosen at random for each object, then there are n choices for placing each object. Then, by the multiplication rule, the number of ways of placing all r objects is $n \times n \times \ldots \times n$, where there is a factor n for each of the objects. If we take as sample space S the set of all such ways of placing the r objects, then it contains n^r elements, and the probability of each simple event is $1/n^r$. Now we modify the problem by assuming that the r objects look alike. Then some of the elements of S become indistinguishable. We have already seen an example of this effect in the special case of putting 2 objects into 3 cells: The outcomes $| | a | b |$ and $| | b | a |$ are distinguishable when the two objects are distinguishable. But if a and b are replaced by $*$, the outcomes become | | $*$ | $*$ | and | | $*$ | $*$ | and are indistinguishable. Outcomes that look different when distinguishable objects are used look the same when indistinguishable objects are used if and only if the outcomes have the same occupancy numbers. If we form a new sample space T containing all distinguishable outcomes that are possible when indistinguishable objects are used, then there is one and only one element of T for each possible set of occupancy numbers. Each element of T corresponds to one or more elements of S which have the same occupancy numbers. Let x be the number of elements of S that have the same occupancy numbers $r_1, r_2, \ldots, r_n$ as a particular element of T. Then the probability of the simple event of T that contains that element is x/n^r. Since the number x may be 1 or more than 1, the simple events in T are not all equally likely. Finding out what the number x is for each element of T is a counting problem that we shall take up in the next chapter.

Let us return to the problem of putting 2 objects that look alike into 3 cells. There are 6 possible distinguishable outcomes in the sample space T shown on page 49. We now change our assumptions about the experiment as follows: *assume that the distinguishable outcomes are all equally likely.* This assumption implies a new assignment of probabilities to the simple events in T: the probability of each simple event is $\frac{1}{6}$. Let us call this new probability model *cell model II*. It has the same sample space as cell model I, but whereas in model I the possible outcomes are not equally likely, in model II they are. We can generalize cell model II by considering again the problem of putting r objects that look alike into n cells. If we denote by T the sample space for the generalized model, then $n(T)$ stands for the number of possible distinguishable outcomes. Since we are now assuming that these outcomes are equally likely, the probability of each simple event in the generalized model is $1/n(T)$. Finding the number $n(T)$

is another counting problem that we shall solve in the
next chapter.

Let us consider once more the problem of putting 2
objects that look alike into 3 cells, with a new change in
our assumptions. Assume now, first, that *no two objects
are placed in the same cell*, and secondly, that all possible
distinguishable outcomes are equally likely. Under these
assumptions we cannot use the sample space T of page 49,
because the outcomes shown there on the first line cannot
occur. We have, instead, a smaller sample space W as
follows:

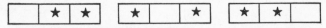

**Possible distinguishable outcomes when 2 objects that look
alike are put into 3 cells and no cell gets more than one
element (sample space W)**

Because these outcomes are equally likely, we assign
these probabilities: $P(\{|\ |\ *\ |\ *\ |\}) = \frac{1}{3}, P(\{|\ *\ |\ |\ *\ |\}) = \frac{1}{3}$,
and $P(\{|\ *\ |\ *\ |\ |\}) = \frac{1}{3}$. Let us call this new probability
model *cell model III*. It differs from cell model II in that
certain outcomes in cell model II have been excluded from
the sample space. We can generalize cell model III, provided that we assume that the number of objects r is not
more than the number of cells n. If we denote the sample
space of the generalized model by W, then W consists
of those elements of T that are *permitted* by the rule that
no two elements are in the same cell. Then $n(W)$ is the
number of *permitted* distinguishable outcomes. Since they
are assumed to be equally likely, the probability of each
simple event in W is $1/n(W)$. Finding the number $n(W)$
is another counting problem that we postpone until the
next chapter.

A problem like that of putting r objects that look alike
into n cells arises in contemporary physics. The objects
that look alike may be a set of r identical atoms, or r identical nuclei, or r electrons, etc. The n cells into which they

are placed are n possible energy states. Which of the cell models, I, II, or III, should the physicist use? This is a question that cannot be answered on the basis of intuition alone. The answer has to be based on experimental evidence obtained in the physics laboratory. The answer, in fact, is a surprising one. Our intuition, based on our experience with activities like putting letters into boxes, favors model I. The physicists Maxwell and Boltzmann had used this model successfully during the nineteenth century when they studied the different ways in which the molecules of a gas may be distributed among different energy levels. For this reason, physicists refer to cell model I as *Maxwell-Boltzmann statistics*. During the twentieth century, when physicists tried to apply Maxwell-Boltzmann statistics to the study of small particles, like atoms, nuclei, electrons, protons, and so on, they failed. They found that they could describe the behavior of these small particles successfully only if they used cell model II or cell model III. Cell model II, which physicists call *Bose-Einstein statistics*, applies to photons and to nuclei and atoms with an even number of elementary particles in them. (The number of elementary particles in an atom is the number of neutrons in its nucleus + the number of protons in its nucleus + the number of electrons that surround the nucleus.) Cell model III, which physicists call *Fermi-Dirac statistics*, applies to electrons, neutrons and protons, and to nuclei and atoms with an odd number of elementary particles in them.

The Birthday Problem. We end this chapter by solving a well-known problem with the help of a probability model based on putting objects into cells. Here is the problem: Suppose there are r people in a room. What is the smallest value of r that assures that there is a better than even chance (probability greater than $\frac{1}{2}$) that at least two people in the room have the same birthday? The answer turns out to be a surprising one to most people. We shall work our way towards the answer in a series of easy steps. We shall let r be successively 2, 3, 4, and so on, and for each value of r we shall calculate the probability that at least two people in the room have the same birthday. We shall obtain in this way a series of increasing probabilities. The first value of r for which this probability is greater than $\frac{1}{2}$ is the answer to our question.

We shall assume for the purpose of solving this problem that each year has 365 days. Think of each day as a cell. Attaching a birthday to each person in the room is like putting each person into a cell. For each value of r we want to calculate the probability that at least one cell will contain 2 or more people.

If $r = 2$, we are putting 2 objects into 365 cells. Put one object at a time into its cell. We may put the first object into any one of 365 cells. We may also put the second object into any one of 365 cells. Therefore we have 365 $\times$ 365 ways of choosing cells for the pair. We take as sample space the set of all 365^2 possible outcomes, and assume that they are all equally likely. The probability of the event E that at least one cell has 2 or more objects will be $n(E)/365^2$. To find $n(E)$ we shall first calculate $n(E')$, the number of elements that are not in E, because $n(E) = 365^2 - n(E')$, (that is, it is the number of elements in the sample space that are left after we remove those elements that are not in E). E' may be described as the event that no cell has more than one object in it. Each element of E' may be thought of as the outcome of a compound experiment made up of two steps carried out in succession: step one, put the first object into a cell; step two, place the second object into a cell not already occupied by the first object. Step one can be carried out in any one of 365 ways, since we have 365 cells to choose from. After the completion of step one there will be only 364 empty cells. So step two can be carried out in any one of 364 ways. The compound experiment can be carried out in 365 $\times$ 364 ways. So $n(E') = 365 \times 364$. Then $n(E) = 365^2 - (365 \times$

364) $= 365(365 - 364) = 365$. Consequently $P(E) = 365/365^2 = 1/365 = .003$ approximately.

If $r = 3$, we are putting 3 objects into 365 cells. The sample space consists of 365^3 equally likely outcomes. Define E and E' as we did above. This time $n(E) = 365^3 - n(E')$, and $P(E) = n(E)/365^3$. To calculate $n(E')$, think of each element of E' as the outcome of a compound experiment made up of three steps carried out in succession: step one, put the first object into a cell; step two, put the second object into a cell not already occupied by the first object; step three, put the third object into a cell not already occupied by either of the first two objects. These three steps can be carried out in 365, 364, and 363 ways respectively. Therefore $n(E') = 365 \times 364 \times 363$. $n(E) = 365^3 - (365 \times 364 \times 363) = 365 \times 1093$. Then $P(E) = (365 \times 1093)/365^3 = 1093/365^2 = 1093/133225 = .008$ approximately.

By similar reasoning, we get the following values of $P(E)$ for higher values of r:

for $r = 4$, $n(E) = 365^4 - (365 \times 364 \times 363 \times 362)$, and $P(E) = n(E)/365^4$; for $r = 5$, $n(E) = 365^5 - (365 \times 364 \times 363 \times 362 \times 361)$, and $P(E) = n(E)/365^5$; etc.

The values of $P(E)$ for some different values of r are shown in the table below:

r	10	20	22	23	24	30	50
$P(E)$	.12	.41	.48	.51	.54	.71	.97

The table shows that the answer to the birthday problem is $r = 23$. If there are 23 people in a room there is a better than even chance that at least two people in the room have the same birthday. If there are 50 people in the room there are 97 chances out of a hundred that at least two people in the room have the same birthday.

Exercises for Chapter III

1. Construct a sample space for the experiment of tossing four fair coins, and assign appropriate probabilities to the simple events in the sample space. Let E_0 = the event that no heads turn up, E_1 = the event that exactly one head turns up, E_2 = the event that exactly two heads turn up, E_3 = the event that exactly three heads turn up, and E_4 = the event that four heads turn up. List the elements in E_0, E_1, E_2, E_3, and E_4. Find $n(E_0)$, $n(E_1)$, $n(E_2)$, $n(E_3)$, and $n(E_4)$. Find $P(E_0)$, $P(E_1)$, $P(E_2)$, $P(E_3)$, and $P(E_4)$.

2. A ball is chosen at random from an urn containing 2 white balls and 4 red balls. Construct a two element sample space for the experiment, and assign appropriate probabilities to the simple events in the space. What are the odds in favor of drawing a white ball?

3. A ball is chosen at random from an urn containing 2 white balls, 3 black balls, and 4 red balls. Construct a three element sample space for the experiment, and assign appropriate probabilities to the simple events in the space. What is the probability that a ball drawn is white or black?

4. Three balls are drawn at random without replacement from an urn containing 3 white balls and 2 black balls. Denote the balls by w_1, w_2, w_3, b_1, b_2. Construct a sample space for the experiment, and assign appropriate probabilities to the simple events in the space. Let E_3 = the event that all 3 balls drawn are white, E_2 = the event that exactly 2 out of the 3 balls drawn are white, and E_1 = the event that exactly 1 out of the 3 balls drawn is white. Find $P(E_1)$, $P(E_2)$, and $P(E_3)$.

5. Construct a sample space for fair rolling of a pair of fair dice, and assign appropriate probabilities to the simple events in the space. Let E_n = the event that the sum of the numbers that turn up is n, where n may be 2, 3, 4, 5, 6, or 7. List the elements of E_n for each value of n. Find $P(E_n)$ for each value of n.

6. If a card is drawn at random from a bridge deck, what is the probability that the ace of spades is drawn? That an ace is drawn? That a spade is drawn? That a jack or queen is drawn?

7. Construct a Maxwell-Boltzmann model, a Bose-Einstein model, and a Fermi-Dirac model for the experiment of putting 2 pennies into 4 cells.

8. There are r people in a room, and each one thinks of an integer from 1 to 10. For each value of r from 2 to 10, find the probability that at least two people think of the same number. What is the smallest value of r for which this probability is greater than $\frac{1}{2}$. (Hint: Use the same reasoning employed to solve the birthday problem.)

9. Prove that $\dfrac{r + t}{r + s + t}$ is greater than $\dfrac{r}{r + s}$, where r, s, and t are all positive integers.

CHAPTER IV

Counting and Computing

IF a sample space S consists of equally likely possible outcomes, and E is an event in S, then $P(E) = n(E)/n(S)$. For this reason we often have to count the number of elements in an event. If the number of elements is small, and the elements are listed one by one, we can easily count them one by one. But, in many problems that we shall encounter, the number of elements in an event will be so large that it would be impractical to list them one by one. Often the elements will be identified only by some general description of their properties. In cases like these it is necessary to count the number of elements in an event without listing them. We have to find in the description of the event some clues that enable us to calculate the number of elements that are in it. In this chapter we derive some formulas that can be used for this purpose.

The Multiplication Rule

The foundation of all the formulas we shall derive is the multiplication rule that was stated on page 31: If a compound experiment consists of a sequence of r experiments, and the numbers of possible outcomes of these separate experiments are $n_1, n_2, \ldots, n_r$ respectively, then the number of possible outcomes of the compound experiment is $n_1 \times n_2 \times \ldots \times n_r$. This rule suggests a standard technique for counting the possible outcomes of an experiment: *Break the experiment down into a sequence of small steps.*

Count the number of possible outcomes of each step. Then multiply these numbers.

Putting r Different Things into n Cells

In how many different ways can r different objects be placed in n cells? We have already answered this question on page 50. We review our answer here in order to show how the standard technique for counting was used to get the answer.

To help us see the experiment of placing r things into n cells as a *compound* experiment, we imagine that the r things are numbered from 1 to r. Then we can carry out the experiment in r steps as follows: step 1, place the first thing into a cell; step 2, place the second thing into a cell; step 3, place the third thing into a cell; and so on, until we reach step r, place the r'th thing into a cell. Now we count the number of possible outcomes of each step. In step 1, we can place the first thing into any one of n cells. So there are n possible outcomes. In step 2, we are free to place the second thing into any one of the n cells. So this step, too, has n possible outcomes. At each step, in fact, we may put the object into any one of the n cells. So every one of the r steps has n possible outcomes. Now we multiply the numbers of possible outcomes for the separate steps. We get a product of r factors each of which is equal to n. This product is n^r. So we have our first important counting formula: *The number of ways of putting r different things into n cells is n^r.*

The Number of Subsets of a Set

This formula can be used to answer the question raised in Chapter II, exercise 3: How many subsets does a set with r elements have? When we choose a subset from a set of r elements, we are really dividing the set into two parts. One part consists of the elements that we *take*, or include in the subset. The other part consists of the elements that we *leave*, or exclude from the subset. We can visualize this take it or leave it procedure by imagining that there are two cells, one marked *take it*, and the other marked *leave it*. We choose a subset from among the r elements by putting the elements into the two cells. Then the subset we have chosen consists of the elements that are in the *take it* cell. We get all possible subsets by putting

Subset obtained

Take	Leave
a	bc

{a}

Take	Leave
b	ac

{b}

Take	Leave
c	ab

{c}

Take	Leave
ab	c

{a,b}

Take	Leave
ac	b

{a,c}

Take	Leave
bc	a

{b,c}

Take	Leave
abc	

{a,b,c} = S

Take	Leave
	abc

ϕ

Take it or leave it procedure for forming all the possible subsets of $S = \{a,b,c\}$; $n(S) = 2^3 = 8$

the r elements into the two cells in all possible ways. So the number of subsets of a set of r elements is the number of ways in which the r elements can be put into 2 cells. According to our formula, this number is 2^r. Hence, the empty set, which has 0 elements, has $2^0 = 1$ subset. A set with 1 element has $2^1 = 2$ subsets. A set with 2 elements has $2^2 = 4$ subsets. A set with 3 elements has $2^3 = 8$ subsets, and so on.

Arrangements in a Line

A club with 5 members has 3 elected officers: chairman, secretary, and treasurer. In how many ways may the officers be chosen from the membership of the club? This question can be restated in terms of putting objects into cells. Imagine that there are 3 cells, one for each of the elective offices. Then selecting a set of officers is like putting members of the club into the cells, with the understanding that each cell is to receive one and only one member. To visualize the solution of the problem of counting the number of ways in which this can be done, think of the cells as being arranged in a line. The experiment of putting three people into these cells, one in each cell, may be broken down into 3 steps that are carried out one after the other. Step 1: Choose a person for the first cell. Since there are 5 members in the club, this choice can be made in 5 ways. Step 2: After the completion of step 1, choose a person for the second cell. Since one person has already been chosen for the first cell, only four people are left to choose from for the second cell. So this choice can be made in 4 ways. Step 3: After the completion of steps 1 and 2, choose a person for the third cell. Since two people have already been chosen for the first two cells, only three people are left to choose from for the third cell. So this choice can be made in 3 ways. Then the compound experiment of choosing three officers may be performed in $5 \times 4 \times 3$ ways, or 60 ways.

The problem of selecting three officers is a special case of this more general problem: In how many ways can r cells be filled with one object per cell selected from a set of n objects? (To be able to provide one object per cell, n must be greater than or equal to r.) An equivalent formulation of the problem is this: In how many ways can r objects be selected from a set of n objects and arranged in a line to form an ordered r-tuple? These two formulations are equivalent because each place in a line may be thought of as a cell, and vice versa. We can solve the general problem in the same way that we solved the special case. The experiment of arranging in a line r out of n objects may be broken down into a sequence of r steps. Step 1: Choose an object for the first place in the line. Since we have n objects to choose from, the choice can be made in n ways. Step 2: After the completion of step 1, choose an object for the second place in line. Since one object has already been chosen for the first place, only $n - 1$ objects are left to choose from for the second place. So this choice can be made in $n - 1$ ways. Continue in this way, in steps 3 to r, filling one place in the line at a time, until the r'th place has been filled. Each step reduces the number of unplaced objects by 1, and so reduces by 1 the number of choices available for the next step. Step 3 can be done in $n - 2$ ways, step 4 can be done in $n - 3$ ways, and so on. Step r, the last step, can be done in $n - r + 1$ ways. Then the number of ways of performing the compound experiment is

$$n(n - 1)(n - 2) \ldots (n - r + 1).$$

An arrangement of objects in a line is called a *permutation* of the objects. The number of permutations of r objects selected from a set of n objects is denoted by $P(n, r)$. So our result is summarized in the statement

$$P(n, r) = n(n - 1)(n - 2) \ldots (n - r + 1).$$

When you use this formula, it is not necessary to remember

the form of the last factor in the product. It suffices to remember that there are r factors, that the first factor is n, and that the others are obtained from n by counting backwards. For example, to compute the number of permutations of 4 things selected from a set of 7 things, write down 4 factors by counting backwards starting with 7: $P(7, 4) = 7 \times 6 \times 5 \times 4 = 840$.

In the special case where all n objects are arranged in a line to form an ordered n-tuple, we have $P(n, n) = n(n - 1)(n - 2) \ldots 1$. This product of n factors from the integer n down to 1 is called n *factorial* and is denoted by $n!$, where the exclamation mark is part of the mathematical symbol and is not used as a sign of excitement. $1! = 1$; $2! = 2 \times 1 = 2; 3! = 3 \times 2 \times 1 = 6; 4! = 4 \times 3 \times 2 \times 1 = 24$; and so on. The definition of $n!$ given above does not apply to $n = 0$. We shall find it useful to extend the definition to $n = 0$ by agreeing to write $0! = 1$.

First place	Second place	Third place	Ordered triple that is formed
a	b	c	(a,b,c)
	c	b	(a,c,b)
b	a	c	(b,a,c)
	c	a	(b,c,a)
c	a	b	(c,a,b)
	b	a	(c,b,a)

Tree diagram for forming all the permutations of 3 out of 3 things; P(3,3) = 3! = 6

A more compact expression for $P(n, r)$ can be obtained by using the factorial notation. We already know that $P(7, 4) = 7 \times 6 \times 5 \times 4$. The value of the product on the right hand side of the equals sign remains unchanged if we multiply it by $\dfrac{3 \times 2 \times 1}{3 \times 2 \times 1}$, since this fraction is equal to 1. Then we have

$$P(7, 4) = \frac{7 \times 6 \times 5 \times 4 \times 3 \times 2 \times 1}{3 \times 2 \times 1} = \frac{7!}{3!}.$$

We can follow a similar procedure with the general formula $P(n, r) = n(n - 1)(n - 2) \ldots (n - r + 1)$. The number that is 1 less than $n - r + 1$ is $n - r$. Multiply the product on the right-hand side of the equals sign by $\dfrac{(n - r)(n - r - 1) \ldots 1}{(n - r)(n - r - 1) \ldots 1}$, which is equal to 1. Then we have $P(n, \ r) = \dfrac{n(n - 1)(n - 2) \ldots 1}{(n - r)(n - r - 1) \ldots 1} = \dfrac{n!}{(n - r)!}.$
This version of the formula will be useful for some purposes.

The Number of Subsets of a Given Size

If a set S contains n elements, how many subsets does it have that contain exactly r elements, where r is any integer from 0 to n? We can answer the question for the extreme cases $r = 0$ and $r = n$ immediately. There is only one subset of S that has 0 elements, namely, the empty set. There is only one subset of S that has all n elements in it, namely, the set S itself. Let us introduce the symbol $\binom{n}{r}$ to represent the number of subsets containing exactly r elements selected from a set of n elements. Then we can say $\binom{n}{0} = 1$, and $\binom{n}{n} = 1$. To find $\binom{n}{r}$ for the cases where r is neither 0 nor n, we return to the problem of calculating $P(n, r)$, and re-examine it from another point of view. Arranging r out of n objects in a line may be thought of as a compound experiment made up of two steps carried out in succession: First select a subset of r objects. Then

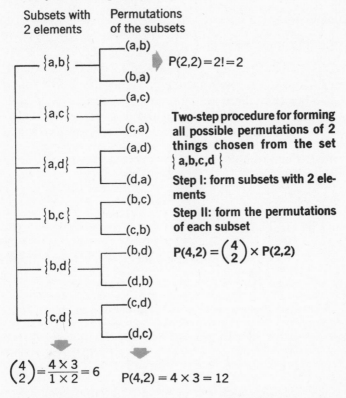

Subsets with 2 elements | Permutations of the subsets

{a,b} → (a,b), (b,a)

$P(2,2) = 2! = 2$

{a,c} → (a,c), (c,a)

{a,d} → (a,d), (d,a)

{b,c} → (b,c), (c,b)

{b,d} → (b,d), (d,b)

{c,d} → (c,d), (d,c)

Two-step procedure for forming all possible permutations of 2 things chosen from the set { a,b,c,d }

Step I: form subsets with 2 elements

Step II: form the permutations of each subset

$P(4,2) = \binom{4}{2} \times P(2,2)$

$\binom{4}{2} = \frac{4 \times 3}{1 \times 2} = 6$ $P(4,2) = 4 \times 3 = 12$

arrange them in a line. Selecting a subset of r objects out of n can be done in $\binom{n}{r}$ ways. Arranging r objects in a line can be done in $P(r, r)$ ways. So $P(n, r) = \binom{n}{r} \times P(r, r)$.

Consequently $\binom{n}{r} = \dfrac{P(n, r)}{P(r, r)}$. This formula takes on two commonly used forms, depending on which version of the formula for $P(n, r)$ we use. We may substitute $n(n - 1) \ldots (n - r + 1)$ for $P(n, r)$, and $r(r - 1) \ldots 1$ for $P(r, r)$. Then, if we write the factors of the numerator in descending order, and the factors of the denominator in ascending order, we have $\binom{n}{r} = \dfrac{n(n-1) \ldots (n-r+1)}{1 \times 2 \times \ldots \ldots \times r}$. This version of the formula is useful for making computations. To use it for any particular values of n and r simply remember that there are r factors in the numerator and r factors in the denominator. In the numerator the factors descend from n. In the denominator the factors ascend from 1. For example, $\binom{7}{3} = \dfrac{7 \times 6 \times 5}{1 \times 2 \times 3} = 35$.

However, we may also write $\dfrac{n!}{(n-r)!}$ for $P(n, r)$, and $r!$ for $P(r, r)$. Then the formula for $\binom{n}{r}$ takes this form: $\binom{n}{r} = \dfrac{n!}{r!(n-r)!}$. If we write s for $n-r$, so that r and s are related by the condition $r + s = n$, we may also write $\binom{n}{r} = \dfrac{n!}{r!s!}$, where $r + s = n$. This version of the formula has the advantage of showing us at a glance that if $r + s = n$, then $\binom{n}{r} = \binom{n}{s}$. For example, $\binom{7}{4} = \dfrac{7 \times 6 \times 5 \times 4}{1 \times 2 \times 3 \times 4} = 35$, which agrees with the value of $\binom{7}{3}$ found above. You can verify easily that the formula is correct even when $r = 0$ or n.

Ordered Subsets of Fixed Size

The formula $\binom{n}{r} = \dfrac{n!}{r!s!}$, where $r + s = n$ suggests another useful interpretation of $\binom{n}{r}$. When we take r objects out of n to form a subset, we leave behind the remaining s objects. These s objects form another subset. So $\binom{n}{r}$ gives us the number of ways in which we can divide n objects into two subsets, the first of which has r objects and the second of which has s objects. We may picture the subsets as being formed by putting the n objects into two cells that are arranged in a line, with r objects in the first cell, and s objects in the second cell. Each such distribution has occupancy numbers r, s, and the number $\binom{n}{r}$ is the number of distributions that have these occupancy numbers. The cell picture tempts us to generalize the formula by using any number of cells instead of using just two cells. Suppose there are k cells arranged in a line, from left to right, and we put all n objects into the cells, so that the distribution has occupancy numbers $r_1, r_2, \ldots, r_k$. It is clear that $r_1 + r_2 + \ldots + r_k = n$, the total number of objects. If we disregard the order of the objects within the cells, in how many ways can this be done? We shall use the symbol $\binom{n}{r_1, r_2, \ldots, r_k}$ to represent the answer to this question. To derive a formula for it, we note that if we arrange the objects in each cell in a line from left to right, then since the cells themselves are in a line from left to right, we end up with a linear arrangement or permutation of all n objects. Then the experiment of arranging the n objects in a line may be viewed as a compound experiment made up of $k + 1$ steps carried out in succession. Step 1, put the n objects into the k cells, in a distribution with occupancy numbers $r_1, r_2, \ldots, r_k$. This can be done in $\binom{n}{r_1, r_2, \ldots, r_k}$ ways. Step 2, arrange the r_1 objects in the first cell in a line. This can be done in $r_1!$ ways. Step 3, arrange the r_2 objects in the second cell in a line. This can be done in $r_2!$ ways. . . . Step $k + 1$, arrange the r_k objects in the k'th cell in a line. This can be done in $r_k!$ ways. Now we can use the multiplication rule to express the number of ways in which the compound experiment of arranging n things in a line may be done. But we already know that this number is $n!$ So we have the equation:

$$n! = \binom{n}{r_1, r_2, \ldots, r_k} \times r_1! \times r_2! \times \ldots \times r_k!.$$

Then we find by division that

$$\binom{n}{r_1, r_2, \ldots, r_k} = \frac{n!}{r_1! r_2! \ldots r_k!}$$

We note that the derivation of this formula is valid even if some of the r's are zero.

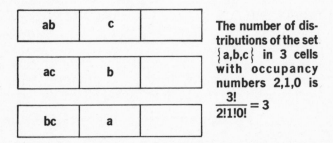

The number of distributions of the set $\{a,b,c\}$ in 3 cells with occupancy numbers 2,1,0 is $\dfrac{3!}{2!1!0!} = 3$

The dealing of cards in a bridge game is an experiment to which this formula may be applied. Of the 52 cards in the deck, 13 cards are dealt to each of the players North, East, South and West. This is like putting the 52 cards into four cells arranged in a line, with 13 cards in each cell. Then we may use the formula with $n = 52, r_1 = r_2 = r_3 = r_4 = 13$. The number of ways in which the cards may be dealt is $\dfrac{52!}{(13!)^4}$.

Tossing a Coin

In Chapter III we considered this question: If a fair coin is tossed k times, what is the probability that exactly r heads (and hence $k - r$ tails) turn up? We let E be the event that exactly r heads turn up, and we found that

$P(E) = n(E)/2^k$. We can now complete the answer by finding what $n(E)$ is. Tossing one coin k times is like tossing k coins once. Tossing k coins is like putting the k coins into two cells one of which is marked *heads* while the other one is marked *tails*. E is the event that exactly r of the coins are put into the cell marked *heads*, while $k - r$ of the coins are put into the cell marked tails, so that the occupancy numbers of the distribution are $r, k - r$. The number of ways in which this can be done is $n(E) = \binom{k}{r} = \dfrac{k!}{r!(k-r)!}$. Consequently $P(E) = \binom{k}{r}/2^k$. For example, if 5 coins are tossed, the probability of getting exactly 3 heads is $\binom{5}{3}/2^5 = \dfrac{10}{32} = \dfrac{5}{16}$, since $\binom{5}{3} = \dfrac{5 \times 4 \times 3}{1 \times 2 \times 3}$, and $2^5 = 2 \times 2 \times 2 \times 2 \times 2$.

Heads	Tails
① ②	③ ④

Heads	Tails
① ③	② ④

Heads	Tails
① ④	② ③

Heads	Tails
② ③	① ④

Heads	Tails
② ④	① ③

Heads	Tails
③ ④	① ②

Four coins ① ② ③ ④ **are tossed. The number of ways of getting 2 heads is**

$$\binom{4}{2} = \binom{4}{2,2} = \frac{4!}{2!2!} = 6$$

Drawing Without Replacement

Another question postponed from Chapter III is this: An urn contains r white balls and s black balls, and k balls are drawn at random without replacement. What is the probability that m of the k balls drawn will be white? We assume that m is no larger than r. The total number of balls in the urn is $r + s$. When k balls are drawn from the urn they constitute a subset with k elements selected from a set with $r + s$ elements. The sample space S for this problem is the set of all such subsets. Then $n(S) = \binom{r + s}{k}$. Let E be the event that m of the k balls are white. When m of the k balls are white, $k - m$ of the balls are black. Choosing balls so that the event E occurs may be thought of as a compound experiment made up of two steps. First step: Choose m balls from among the r white balls in the urn. This can be done in $\binom{r}{m}$ ways. Second step: Choose $k - m$ balls from among the s black balls in the urn. This can be done in $\binom{s}{k - m}$ ways. Then, by the multiplication rule, $n(E) = \binom{r}{m}\binom{s}{k - m}$. Since the elements of S are equally likely, $P(E) = n(E)/n(S) = \binom{r}{m}\binom{s}{k - m}/\binom{r + s}{k}$. For example, if the urn has 3 white balls and 2 black balls, and 3 balls are drawn, the probability that 2 of them are white is obtained from this formula by using $r = 3$, $s = 2$, $k = 3$, and $m = 2$. Then $P(E) = \binom{3}{2}\binom{2}{1}/\binom{5}{3} = \dfrac{6}{10}$. (See diagrams on page 71.)

Maxwell-Boltzmann Statistics

If r objects that look alike are placed in n cells, what is the probability of each distinguishable distribution of the

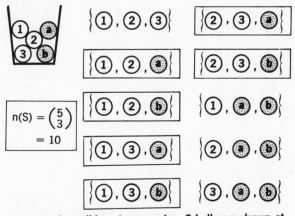

S = set of possible outcomes when 3 balls are drawn at random from an urn containing 3 white balls and 2 black balls

E = set of outcomes with exactly 2 white balls (boxed elements)

Two-step procedure for getting E:

Step I: Pick any 2 of the 3 white balls

Step II: Pick any 1 of the 2 black balls

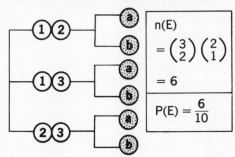

objects? A particular distinguishable distribution of objects that look alike is described completely by specifying the occupancy numbers of the distribution. For example, when we put 2 stars into 3 boxes, the occupancy numbers

2, 0, 0 describe the distribution $|**|\ |\ |$, while the occupancy numbers 1, 0, 1 describe the distribution $|*|\ |*|$. We found on page 51 that the probability of the distribution with occupancy numbers $r_1, r_2, \ldots, r_n$ is x/n^r, where x is the number of ways in which r distinguishable objects can be put into n cells in distributions that have these occupancy numbers. Then x is precisely the number that we have denoted in this chapter by the symbol $\binom{r}{r_1, r_2, \ldots, r_n}$ and whose value is $\dfrac{r!}{r_1!r_2!\ldots r_n!}$. So the probability of a distribution with occupancy numbers $r_1, r_2, \ldots, r_n$ is $x/n^r = \dfrac{r!}{r_1!r_2!\ldots r_n!n^r}$. For the distribution shown in the diagram below, where $r = 5$, $n = 4$, and the occupancy numbers are 2, 2, 1, 0 the probability is $\dfrac{5!}{2!2!1!0!4^5} = \dfrac{120}{4096} = .03$ approximately.

Distribution of 5 objects that look alike in 4 cells with occupancy numbers 2,2,1,0

Bose-Einstein Statistics

When r objects that look alike are put into n cells, let T be the set of distinguishable possible outcomes. In Bose-Einstein statistics it is assumed that the elements of T are equally likely, so the probability of each outcome is $1/n(T)$, as we have already stated on page 51. We are now able to derive a formula for the number $n(T)$.

First let us consider the special case of putting 5 objects that look alike into 4 cells. One of the possible outcomes, with occupancy numbers 2, 2, 1, 0 is shown in the diagram above. Let us represent the 4 cells of the problem by the spaces between 5 vertical bars thus, $|\ |\ |\ |\ |$, and let us represent the 5 objects that are put into the cells by stars. Then the outcome with occupancy numbers 2, 2, 1, 0 can be represented by this sequence of bars and stars: | ** | ** | * | |. There are 10 things in this sequence, 5 bars and 5 stars. Every distribution in 4 cells of 5 objects that look alike can be represented by some sequence of the same 10 things. In every such sequence, the first and last thing must be a bar. To get a sequence, first put down the 2 bars that begin and end the sequence. This leaves 8 more things to be put down in 8 places between the end bars. Five of these 8 things are stars, and the other 3 are bars. Every arrangement of these 8 things corresponds to a distinct distribution of the 5 objects in the 4 cells, and vice versa. For example, if we put all the 5 stars in the first 5 of the 8 places between the end bars, we get the distribution | ***** | | | | with occupancy numbers 5, 0, 0, 0. So the number of possible distributions of the stars in the cells is equal to the number of ways in which the 5 stars and 3 bars can be arranged between the end bars. Each arrangement is fixed by choosing the 5 out of the 8 places that are to be filled with stars. This can be done in $\binom{8}{5}$ ways. So the number of possible distributions is $\binom{8}{5} = 56$.

We may use the same reasoning to solve the general problem of counting the distinguishable outcomes when r objects that look alike are put into n cells. The n cells may be represented by the n spaces between $n + 1$ vertical bars, and the r objects may be represented by r stars. Each possible outcome is represented by a sequence of the bars and stars that begins and ends with a bar. To get a particular outcome, first put down the 2 bars that begin and end the sequence. This leaves $n - 1$ bars and r stars, or a total of $n + r - 1$ things to be arranged in as many places between the end bars. A particular outcome is fixed by choosing the r places out of the available

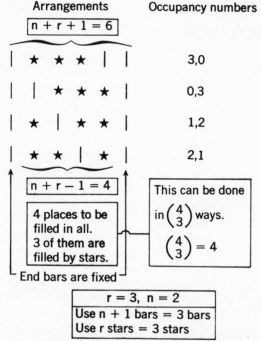

Bars and stars procedure for finding all possible outcomes when 3 objects that look alike are put into 2 cells

$n + r - 1$ places that are to be filled with stars. This can be done in $\binom{n + r - 1}{r}$ ways. Therefore $n(T) = \binom{n + r - 1}{r}$, and the probability of each simple event in T is $1 / \binom{n + r - 1}{r}$. For the distribution shown in the diagram on page 72, $n = 4$ and $r = 5$, and $n(T) = 56$. Under Bose-Einstein statistics, when 5 objects that look alike are put into 4 cells, the probability of each of these outcomes is $1/56 = .02$ approximately, no matter what the occupancy numbers of the outcome may be. Under Maxwell-Boltzmann statistics, however, the probability depends on the occupancy numbers.

If $r = 2$ and $n = 3$, $n(T) = \binom{3 + 2 - 1}{2} = \binom{4}{2} = 6$.

This is confirmed by the diagram for T in this case, shown on page 49.

Fermi-Dirac Statistics

When r objects that look alike are put into n cells in such a way that *no cell contains more than one object*, the distribution is possible only if r is not greater than n. Let W be the set of distinguishable possible outcomes obtained under these conditions. In Fermi-Dirac statistics it is assumed that the elements of W are equally likely, so the probability of each of them is $1/n(W)$, as already stated on page 52. To derive a formula for $n(W)$ it is sufficient to point out that putting r objects into n cells, with at most one object per cell, means picking out r cells to receive the r objects. Each distribution of the objects therefore corresponds to a subset of r cells chosen from the n cells, and vice versa. Therefore $n(W)$ is equal to the number of such subsets, or $\binom{n}{r}$. Consequently the probability of each simple event in W is $1/\binom{n}{r}$.

If $r = 2$ and $n = 3$, $n(T) = \binom{3}{2} = 3$. This is confirmed by the diagram for W in this case, shown on page 52.

The Binomial Theorem

When you expand the product $(a + b)(c + d)$, you get $ac + ad + bc + bd$. Notice that the expansion is the sum of 4 terms. Each term has two factors. One of the factors is a term of the first set of parentheses, that is, it is a or b. The other factor is a term of the second set of parentheses, that is, it is c or d. We get all possible terms of the product by choosing in all possible ways a term from the first set of parentheses and a term from the second set of parentheses and multiplying them. This observation suggests a way in which we could have predicted the number of terms there would be in the product. Forming a term of the product is a compound experiment made up of two steps. Step one is choosing a or b as a factor. This can be done in 2 ways. Step 2 is choosing c or d as a factor. This can be done in 2 ways. Therefore the compound experiment can be carried out in 2×2 or 2^2 ways.

If c is replaced by a, and d is replaced by b, the product becomes $(a + b)(a + b)$, which we may write as $(a + b)^2$, and the expansion becomes $aa + ab + ba + bb$. We may write aa as $1a^2$, and bb as $1b^2$. Moreover, since $ab = ba$, we may write the sum $ab + ba$ as $2ab$. Then we have $(a + b)^2 = 1a^2 + 2ab + 1b^2$. We shall now derive this result in another way that we shall be able to generalize. When we expand $(a + b)(a + b)$, we already know from the paragraph above that the expansion will contain 2^2 or 4 terms. Each term will have two factors. One of the factors is either a or b, chosen from the first set of parentheses. The other factor is also either a or b, but is chosen from the second set of parentheses. The terms of the product may be classified by the kinds of factors they have. The two factors may be both a, or one factor may be a while the other factor is b, or both factors may be b. To get the first case, (both factors a), we are required to choose a from both sets of parentheses. This can be done in only 1 way, so there is only term of the form a^2. That is why its coefficient in the expansion is 1. To get the second case, (one factor is a while the other factor is b), we need only choose a from one of the two parentheses and choose b from the other. This can be done in two ways, since a may be chosen from the first or the second set of parentheses. Consequently there are two terms of the form ab. That is why its coefficient in the expansion is 2. To get the third case, (both factors b), we have to choose a from none of the parentheses and b from all of them. This, too, can be done in only one way. So there is only 1 term of the form b^2, and its coefficient in the expansion is 1.

Let us now use the same reasoning to expand the product $(a + b)(a + b)(a + b)$, which we may write as $(a + b)^3$. Each term of the expansion will be a product of 3 factors, one chosen from each set of parentheses. Each of these factors, of course, will be a or b. Since we have 2 ways of choosing the first factor, 2 ways of choosing the second factor, and 2 ways of choosing the third factor, we may form $2 \times 2 \times 2$ or 2^3 terms in this way, a total of 8 terms. However, some of them will be like terms, and may be combined into a single term. The coefficient of each kind of term will be the number of terms like it that occur among the 8 terms of the expansion.

Each term is a product of 3 factors. If we classify the terms by the number of factors that are a's, we find that there are these possible outcomes: all 3 factors are a's, in which case the term has the form a^3; 2 factors are a's, in which case the term has the form a^2b; 1 factor is an a, in which case the term has the form ab^2; 0 factors are a's, in which case the term has the form b^3. Now we proceed to find out how many terms of each kind there are. To get 3 factors that are a's, we must choose a as the factor from each of the 3 parentheses. That is, we pick 3 sets of parentheses out of 3 as the ones from which we may choose a as a factor. This can be done in $\binom{3}{3}$ ways. So there are $\binom{3}{3}$ terms of the form a^3. Then the coefficient of a^3 in the expansion is $\binom{3}{3} = 1$. To get 2 factors that are a's, we must choose a as the factor from each of 2 parentheses. That is, we pick 2 sets of parentheses out of 3 as the ones from which we may choose a as a factor. This can be done in $\binom{3}{2}$ ways. So there are $\binom{3}{2}$ terms of the form a^2b. Then the coefficient of a^2b in the expansion is $\binom{3}{2} = 3$. To get 1 factor that is a, we must choose a as the factor from only one of the parentheses. That is, we pick 1 set of parentheses out of 3 as the one from which we may choose a as a factor. This can be done in $\binom{3}{1}$ ways. So there are $\binom{3}{1}$ terms of the form ab^2. Then the coefficient of ab^2 in the expansion is $\binom{3}{1} = 3$. To get 0 factors that are a's, we must choose a as the factor from none of the parentheses. That is, we choose 0 sets of parentheses out of 3 as the ones from which we may choose a as a factor. This can be done in $\binom{3}{0}$ ways. So there are $\binom{3}{0}$ terms of the form b^3. Then the coefficient of b^3 in the expansion is $\binom{3}{0} = 1$. Consequently

$$(a + b)^3 = \binom{3}{3} a^3 + \binom{3}{2} a^2b + \binom{3}{1} ab^2 + \binom{3}{0} b^3,$$
$$or \ (a + b)^3 = 1a^3 + 3a^2b + 3ab^2 + b^3.$$

We can now generalize this result easily. If the product $(a + b)(a + b) \ldots (a + b)$ has n factors of the form $(a + b)$, then we may write it as $(a + b)^n$. Each term of the expansion for this product will contain n factors, one chosen from each set of parentheses. Each of these factors will be a or b. Since we have 2 choices in each of n parentheses, we may form the terms in 2^n ways. Some of the terms will be like terms, and may be combined into a single term. The coefficient of each kind of term will be the number of terms like it that occur among the 2^n terms of the expansion.

Each term is a product of n factors. The number of factors that are a's may be any number r ranging from 0 to n. If r of the factors are a's, then $n - r$ of the factors are b's, and the term has the form $a^r b^{n-r}$. To get r factors that are a's, we must choose a as the factor from each of r parentheses. That is, we pick r sets of parentheses out of n as the ones frm which we may choose a as a factor. This can be done in $\binom{n}{r}$ ways. So there are $\binom{n}{r}$ terms of the form $a^r b^{n-r}$. Then the coefficient of $a^r b^{n-r}$ in the expansion is $\binom{n}{r}$. To get the coefficients of successive terms in the expansion when it is written in descending powers of a, simply let r range through the integers from n to 0. Consequently,

$$(a + b)^n = \binom{n}{n} a^n + \binom{n}{n-1} a^{n-1}b + \cdots$$
$$+ \binom{n}{n-r} a^{n-r}b^r + \cdots + \binom{n}{0} b^n.$$

Since $\binom{n}{r} = \binom{n}{n-r}$, this expansion may also be written in this form:

$$(a + b)^n = \binom{n}{0} a^n + \binom{n}{1} a^{n-1}b + \cdots$$
$$+ \binom{n}{r} a^{n-r}b^r + \cdots + \binom{n}{n} b^n.$$

The latter form can be obtained directly by the same argument that led to the first form, provided that we keep track of where the b factors come from rather than where the a factors come from. The result expressed in the equations above is known as the *binomial theorem*. It is for this reason that the numbers $\binom{n}{r}$ are known as *binomial coefficients*. We have already used them many times to solve probability problems. We shall use them many more times in later chapters.

A Pin-Ball Machine Model

The expansion of $(a + b)^n$ can be represented by an interesting pin-ball machine model. The machine consists of nails hammered into a board in the arrangement shown in the diagram. The spaces between adjacent nails are just wide enough to allow a small ball to pass through. The board is tilted with respect to the horizontal plane, and a ball is allowed to roll down from the top of the board towards the center nail in the first row of nails. After striking the nail, the ball passes through the first row of nails by going right or left. The numbers 1, 1 written in the spaces in the first row of nails show the number of paths that the ball may follow to reach those positions. They correspond to the outcomes *left* or *right*, which we may designate by the letters L and R. After passing through the first row of nails the ball must again "choose" whether to go right or left on its way through the second row of nails. Where the ball emerges from the second row of nails depends on its choices at *both* rows of nails. If the ball goes left through the first row and left through the second row,

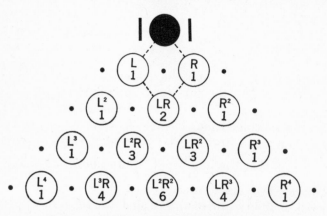

**Paths and outcomes in a pin-ball machine
(Pascal's triangle)**

it emerges from the first space in the second row. Call this position LL or L^2. If the ball goes left through the first row and right through the second row, or right through the first row and left through the second row, it emerges from the second space in the second row. Call this position LR. The paths that lead to it are shown by the dotted lines. If the ball goes right through the first row and right through the second row, it emerges from the third space in the second row. Call this position RR or R^2. The numbers in these positions indicate the number of paths that lead to it. The numbers are the coefficients of the terms L^2, LR, and R^2 in the expansion of $(L + R)^2$. This is not surprising, in view of the fact that the ball must choose to go left or right through each of the two rows, just as we have to choose L or R as factors from each of the two parentheses when we expand $(L + R)^2$. To pass through three rows of nails, the ball must make the choice left or right 3 times. If it chooses left all three times, it emerges from the first space in the third row. So we designate this space by L^3. If it chooses left twice, and right only once, it emerges from the second space. So we designate this space by L^2R. Similarly the third space is LR^2, and the last space is R^3. How many paths lead to each of these positions? The ball can reach L^3 from the second line only if it passes through L^2 there. There is only 1 path leading to L^2, so there is only 1 path that leads to L^3, namely a prolongation of the one that led to L^2. A ball can reach L^2R from two positions in the line above it. It might come from L^2 and then move right, or it might come from LR and then move left. Since there is 1 path leading to L^2 and there are 2 paths leading to LR, there are $1 + 2$ paths leading to L^2R. The argument we have just used can be generalized. A ball can reach any position in a row below the first row only by first passing through one of the two positions nearest it in the row above it. The new position lies under and between these two earlier positions from which the ball may have come. To find the number of paths that lead to any position add the numbers of the paths that lead to these two positions that feed it. Thus the number of paths that lead to LR^2 is $2 + 1 = 3$, and the number of paths that lead to R^3 is 1. By using this scheme of calculation, once we know how many paths lead to each space in a row, we can calculate the number of paths that lead to each space in the next row. The triangular array of numbers obtained in this way is called *Pascal's triangle*. The numbers on the n'th row are the coefficients that appear in the expansion of $(L + R)^n$ by the binomial theorem. Since we already know that the coefficient of $L^{n-r}R^r$ is $\binom{n}{r}$, we can also display the triangle in the form shown below.

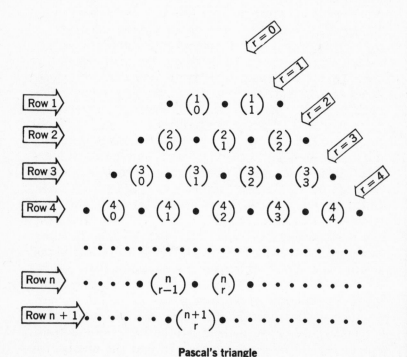

Pascal's triangle

Properties of the Binomial Coefficients

The binomial coefficients have many interesting and useful properties. We shall take note of only three of them here.

The first property we call attention to is one that we have already noted and used, namely that $\binom{n}{r} = \binom{n}{n-r}$. This property is useful for shortening computations. For example, the formula for $\binom{7}{5}$ requires us to write the fraction $\dfrac{7 \times 6 \times 5 \times 4 \times 3}{1 \times 2 \times 3 \times 4 \times 5}$, which has five factors in both the numerator and the denominator. However, since $\binom{7}{5} = \binom{7}{2}$, we can write instead the fraction $\dfrac{7 \times 6}{1 \times 2}$, which has only two factors in the numerator and denominator.

The second property is one that is immediately evident from our derivation of the binomial theorem. When we expanded the product $(a + b)^n$, we noted first that there are 2^n terms in the expansion. The coefficient $\binom{n}{r}$ is the number of terms of the form $a^{n-r}b^r$. If we add all the coefficients for fixed n, with values of r ranging from 0 to n, we get the total number of terms. So,

$$\binom{n}{0} + \binom{n}{1} + \binom{n}{2} + \ldots\ldots\ldots + \binom{n}{n} = 2^n.$$

We can arrive at the same conclusion in a second way noting that the equation

$$(a + b)^n = \binom{n}{0} a^n + \binom{n}{1} a^{n-1}b$$
$$+ \binom{n}{2} a^{n-2}b^2 + \ldots + \binom{n}{n} b^n$$

is true for all values of a and b. In particular, it is true when $a = 1$ and $b = 1$. Substituting these values for a and b, the left-hand side of the equation becomes $(1 + 1)^n$, which is 2^n, while the right hand side of the equation becomes the sum of the binomial coefficients for fixed n.

There is a third way, too, of getting this result. We know from page 64 that $\binom{n}{r}$ is the number of subsets containing r things selected from n things. If we let r take on all possible integral values from 0 to n, and add the resulting coefficients, the sum is the total number of subsets that can be formed from n things. But we already know from page 61 that this total number is 2^n.

The third property of the binomial coefficients that we shall observe is evident in the structure of Pascal's triangle. We have already seen that if you add two adjacent numbers in the same horizontal row of the triangle, you get the number that is between them in the next row. Applying this rule to the three numbers shown in the last two lines in the diagram on page 82, we get $\binom{n}{r-1} + \binom{n}{r} = \binom{n+1}{r}$.

Pascal's Triangle and Tossing a Coin

Pascal's triangle may be interpreted as a probability model for repeated tossings of a fair coin. When a coin is tossed, there are two possible outcomes, T or H. These correspond to the two possible paths, L or R, that a ball in the pin-ball machine may take when it passes through a single row of nails. Tossing a coin n times is like having the ball pass through n rows. The sample space S for n tosses may be taken as the set of all possible paths that lead from the top of the machine through the n'th row. These paths are all equally likely. Let E be the event that r heads and $n - r$ tails turn up. This event corresponds to the place in the n'th row that is marked $L^{n-r}R^r$. The number of elements in this event, $n(E)$, is equal to the number of paths that lead to this place. So $n(E) = \binom{n}{r}$. The *total* number of paths to the n'th line is $n(S)$, and this is, as we know, 2^n. So $P(E) = n(E)/S(E) = \binom{n}{r}/2^n$. This, of course, is the same result we got before on page 69.

The Number *e*

There is a special number that plays an important part in some of the formulas and computations that occur later in this book. We shall borrow results from algebra and the calculus in order to introduce this number and some of its properties.

In textbooks on algebra it is shown that if P dollars are invested at $r\%$ interest for a term of t years, and the interest is compounded n times a year, then the sum of principal and interest at the end of the t years is $A = P\left(1 + \dfrac{r}{100n}\right)^{nt}$ dollars. Let us apply this formula to the case where \$1 is invested at 100% interest for 1 year. Then we let $P = 1$, $r = 100$, and $t = 1$. Then the formula takes on the special form $A = \left(1 + \dfrac{1}{n}\right)^n$. If $n = 2$, (interest compounded semi-annually), $A = (1.5)^2 = 2.25$. If $n = 3$, (interest compounded three times a year), $A = (\frac{4}{3})^3 = \frac{64}{27} = 2.37$ approximately. If $n = 4$, (interest compounded quarterly), $A = (\frac{5}{4})^4 = \frac{625}{256} = 2.44$ approximately. As n increases, the amount A increases. However, it never gets to be as large as 2.75. In fact, it is shown in calculus textbooks that, as n becomes larger and larger without limit, the value of A approaches a definite limit that is approximately equal to 2.71828. The letter e is used to designate this limit. It is customary to say "n approaches infinity" when we mean "n increases without limit." So the number

e may be defined as the limit of $\left(1 + \dfrac{1}{n}\right)^n$ as n approaches infinity.

The symbol e^{-1} is defined to mean $\dfrac{1}{e}$. It is possible to show by some algebraic manipulation that e^{-1} is the limit of $\left(1 - \dfrac{1}{n}\right)^n$ as n approaches infinity.

In calculus textbooks it is shown that e^x may be represented by an infinite series as follows:

$$e^x = 1 + x + \frac{x^2}{2!} + \frac{x^3}{3!} + \ldots + \frac{x^n}{n!} + \ldots$$

If we let x be 1 and -1 respectively, we get representations of e and e^{-1} by infinite series:

$$e = 1 + 1 + \frac{1}{2!} + \frac{1}{3!} + \ldots + \frac{1}{n!} + \ldots$$

$$e^{-1} = \frac{1}{2!} - \frac{1}{3!} + \frac{1}{4!} - \frac{1}{5!} + \ldots$$

The significance of such a series is that by adding up the first few terms of the series we get an approximate value of the number that the series represents. The more terms we add, the better the approximation is.

An Approximation to $n!$

Since $n!$ occurs so often in probability formulas, we have to be prepared to calculate its value for any positive integer n. If n is small, it is easy enough to compute $n!$ directly by multiplication of the integers from 1 to n. But if n is large this direct computation becomes impractical. For example, when a bridge deck is shuffled, the number of possible arrangements of the cards is 52!. Direct computation of this number would require multiplying all the integers from 1 to 52. Fortunately we can bypass this direct computation by means of *Stirling's formula:*

$n!$ is approximately equal to $(2\pi)^{1/2} n^{n+1/2} e^{-n}$.

When the value given by this formula is used for $n!$, there is always an error, but the percentage error is small, and grows smaller as n increases. The advantage of this formula is that it lends itself easily to logarithmic computation. Readers who are familiar with logarithms will see that

$$\log n! = \tfrac{1}{2} \log (2\pi) + (n + \tfrac{1}{2}) \log n - n \log e.$$

Values of $\log n!$ obtained by using this formula, for values of n from 1 to 75, are shown in the first table below. The

COMMON LOGARITHMS OF FACTORIALS

n	$\log n!$	n	$\log n!$	n	$\log n!$
1	0.0000	26	26.6056	51	66.1906
2	0.3010	27	28.0370	52	67.9067
3	0.7782	28	29.4841	53	69.6309
4	1.3802	29	30.9465	54	71.3633
5	2.0792	30	32.4237	55	73.1037
6	2.8573	31	33.9150	56	74.8519
7	3.7024	32	35.4202	57	76.6077
8	4.6055	33	36.9387	58	78.3712
9	5.5598	34	38.4702	59	80.1420
10	6.5598	35	40.0142	60	81.9202
11	7.6012	36	41.5705	61	83.7055
12	8.6803	37	43.1387	62	85.4979
13	9.7943	38	44.7185	63	87.2972
14	10.9404	39	46.3096	64	89.1034
15	12.1165	40	47.9117	65	90.9163
16	13.3206	41	49.5244	66	92.7359
17	14.5511	42	51.1477	67	94.5620
18	15.8063	43	52.7812	68	96.3945
19	17.0851	44	54.4246	69	98.2333
20	18.3861	45	56.0778	70	100.0784
21	19.7083	46	57.7406	71	101.9297
22	21.0508	47	59.4127	72	103.7870
23	22.4125	48	61.0939	73	105.6503
24	23.7927	49	62.7841	74	107.5196
25	25.1907	50	64.4831	75	109.3946

second table is an abbreviated table of common logarithms.

COMMON LOGARITHMS

	0	1	2	3	4	5	6	7	8	9
1	0000	0414	0792	1139	1461	1761	2041	2304	2553	2788
2	3010	3222	3424	3617	3802	3979	4150	4314	4472	4624
3	4771	4914	5051	5185	5315	5441	5563	5682	5798	5911
4	6021	6128	6232	6335	6435	6532	6628	6721	6812	6902
5	6990	7076	7160	7243	7324	7404	7482	7559	7634	7709
6	7782	7853	7924	7993	8062	8129	8195	8261	8325	8388
7	8451	8513	8573	8633	8692	8751	8808	8865	8921	8976
8	9031	9085	9138	9191	9243	9294	9345	9395	9445	9494
9	9542	9590	9638	9685	9731	9777	9823	9868	9912	9956

To find log N, first write N in the form $N = x \times 10^y$, where $1 \leq x < 10$.
Then log $N = y + \log x$.
Example: log $3.4 = .5315$

$$340 = 3.4 \times 10^2, \quad \text{so log } 340 = 2.5315$$
$$.034 = 3.4 \times 10^{-2}, \quad \text{so log } .034 = .5315 - 2.$$

To show how these two tables are used, let us find 52!, the number of different arrangements of a bridge deck. In the first table we find that when $n = 52$, log $n! = 67.9067$. From the second table we find that the number whose logarithm is .9067 is approximately 8.07. Then 52! is approximately 8.07×10^{67}. To write this number you would have to write 807 followed by 65 zeros!

Using the Formulas

Model exercises are worked out below to show how the formulas and tables of this chapter may be used to solve some probability problems:

A Husband and Wife Problem. Five married couples are at a buffet dinner. The ten people get on line at random when dinner is served. What is the probability that each man is next to his wife?

Choose as sample space S the set of all possible arrangements of 10 people in a line. Since the people get on line at random, all these arrangements are equally likely. Let E be the event that each man is next to his wife. $P(E) = n(E)/n(S)$. We obtain $n(S)$ immediately from the fact that the number of arrangements of 10 people in a line is 10!. To get $n(E)$, we proceed to build up elements of E by a sequence of 6 steps. Step 1, with each man next to his wife, arrange the couples in line. This can be done in 5! ways. Steps 2 to 6, for each couple separately, either put the man ahead of his wife, or vice versa. Each of these steps can be carried out in 2 ways. Then we get arrangements in which each man is next to his wife in $5! \times 2^5$ ways. So $n(E) = 5! \times 32$. $P(E) = \dfrac{5! \times 32}{10!}$. The steps in the logarithmic computation of $P(E)$ are shown below:

$$\begin{aligned}
\log 5! &= 2.0792 \\
\log 32 &= \underline{1.5051} \\
&\quad\;\, 3.5843 = 13.5843 - 10 \\
\log 10! &= \underline{6.5598} \\
\log P(E) &= 7.0245 - 10 \\
P(E) &= \text{approximately .001.}
\end{aligned}$$

A Poker Problem. What is the probability that a poker hand dealt from a shuffled deck will have three of a kind?

A poker hand is a subset of 5 cards selected from a deck of 52 cards. Choose as sample space S the set of all possible subsets of 5 cards. Then $n(S) = \dbinom{52}{5} = \dfrac{52!}{5!47!}$. Let E be the event that the hand has three of a kind, that is, it consists of 3 cards of one face value and 2 cards of other face values that differ from each other. Think of the experiment of choosing such a hand as a compound experiment made up of five steps. Step 1, choose the face value that is to occur 3 times. This can be done in $\binom{13}{1}$ ways, since there are 13 face values to choose from. Step 2, choose 3 cards that have that face value. This can be done in $\binom{4}{3}$ ways, since there are four such cards to choose from. Step 3, choose 2 face values from the 12 face values not already used. This can be done in $\binom{12}{2}$ ways. Step 4, choose 1 card with one of these 2 face values. This can be done in $\binom{4}{1}$ ways. Step 5, choose 1 card with the other of these 2 face values. This can be done in $\binom{4}{1}$ ways. Then, by the multiplication rule,

$$n(E) = \binom{13}{1}\binom{4}{3}\binom{12}{2}\binom{4}{1}\binom{4}{1} = 13 \times 4 \times 66 \times 4$$
$$\times 4 = 13 \times 66 \times 64.$$

Since all elements of S are equally likely, $P(E) = \dfrac{n(E)}{n(S)} = \dfrac{13 \times 66 \times 64 \times 5! \times 47!}{52!}$. The computation of $P(E)$ follows:

$$
\begin{array}{rl}
\log 13 = & 1.1139 \\
\log 66 = & 1.8195 \\
\log 64 = & 1.8062 \\
\log 5! = & 2.0792 \\
\log 47! = & \underline{59.4127} \\
& 66.2315 = 76.2315 - 10 \\
\log 52! = & \underline{67.9067} \\
\log P(E) = & 8.3248 - 10 \\
P(E) = & \text{approximately } .02.
\end{array}
$$

A Sampling Problem. A jar contains 75 screws of which 5

are defective. If 25 screws are chosen at random (without replacement), what is the probability that exactly one of them is defective?

Choose as sample space S the set of all subsets of 25 screws out of 75. All elements of S are equally likely, and $n(S) = \binom{75}{25} = \dfrac{75!}{25!50!}$. Let E be the event that exactly 1 of the 25 screws is defective. By the formula on page 70,

$$n(E) = \binom{70}{24}\binom{5}{1} = \frac{70!}{24!46!} \times 5.$$

Then $P(E) = \dfrac{70! \times 5 \times 25! \times 50!}{75! \times 24! \times 46!}.$

$$
\begin{array}{ll}
\log 70! = 100.0784 & \log 75! = 109.3946 \\
\log 5 \;\;\;= \;\;\;\;.6990 & \log 24! = 23.7927 \\
\log 25! = 25.1907 & \log 46! = \underline{57.7406} \\
\log 50! = \underline{64.4831} & 190.9279 \\
 190.4512 = 200.4512 - 10 \\
\underline{190.9279} \\
\log P(E) = 9.5233 - 10 \\
P(E) = \text{approximately } .33.
\end{array}
$$

Exercises for Chapter IV

1. Compute $P(5, 2)$, $P(6, 3)$, and $P(5, 5)$.
2. Compute $6!$.
3. Calculate $\log 10!$, using the formula for $\log n!$ that appears on page 87. (Log $10 = 1$. $2\pi =$ approximately 6.28. $e =$ approximately 2.72. Use the table of common logarithms on page 88 to look up $\log 2\pi$ and $\log e$.) Compare your answer with the value found in the table of common logarithms of factorials on page 87.
4. Calculate $\binom{8}{3}$ and $\binom{8}{5}$.

5. In how many ways can 7 different things be put into 3 cells in distributions that have occupancy numbers 2, 2, 3?

6. We found on page 68 that the number of ways of dealing cards for a bridge game is $\dfrac{52!}{(13!)^4}$. Use the tables on pages 87 and 88 to find an approximate value for this number.

7. If 6 fair coins are tossed, what is the probability that exactly 3 of them turn up heads? What is the probability that at least 3 of them turn up heads?

8. If an urn contains 5 white balls and 3 black balls, and 4 balls are drawn at random, what is the probability that exactly 2 of them are white?

9. If 7 accidents occur at random on a highway during one week, what is the probability that one occurs each day of the week?

10. If 4 things that look alike are put into 3 cells, what is the probability that the distribution will have occupancy numbers 2, 1, 1: a) under Maxwell-Boltzmann statistics? b) under Bose-Einstein statistics?

11. Use bars and stars to show all possible distributions in 3 cells of 4 things that look alike.

12. If a printed text contains n letters, of which r are misprints, the distribution of misprints is like a distribution of r things in n cells with at most one of the things in any one cell. Assume that the distribution of misprints follows Fermi-Dirac statistics. Suppose a book with 40 pages of text has 1200 letters per page. If there are 3 misprints in the book, what is the probability that they all occur on the first page?

13. Compute $\binom{5}{0}$, $\binom{5}{1}$, $\binom{5}{2}$, $\binom{5}{3}$, $\binom{5}{4}$ and $\binom{5}{5}$, and verify that their sum is 2^5.

14. Use the scheme described on page 82 to find the fifth line of Pascal's triangle. Compare your answers with the answers to question 13.

15. If 2 boys and 3 girls take random places on a line, what is the probability that the 3 girls are at the head of the line?

16. If a poker hand is selected at random from a deck of cards,

what is the probability that it is a full house (3 cards with one face value and 2 cards with another face value)?

17. There are 5 chocolates and 1 mint in a box. If 2 candies are chosen at random from the box, what is the probability that the mint is one of them?

CHAPTER V

Events Related to Events

THE probability of a non-empty event in a sample space can be calculated directly by adding up the probabilities of all the simple events that are united in it. The purpose of this chapter is to by-pass the direct calculation by developing ways in which the probability of an event can be computed *indirectly* from the probabilities of other events, (not necessarily simple), to which it is related.

To be sure that the context of our discussion is clear, we recall that a sample space is a set of possible outcomes of an experiment. An event is a subset of the sample space. A simple event is one that contains exactly one element. The probability of a simple event is a number that is positive or 0. The sum of the probabilities of all the simple events in a sample space is 1. The probability of the empty set is 0.

The *certain* event is the sample space itself, and is the union of all the simple events in the space. Since the sum of the probabilities of all the simple events is 1, the probability of the certain event is 1. The probability of any other event in the space is greater than or equal to 0 but less than or equal to 1.

The Union of Two Events

If E and F are two events in a sample space, and their probabilities are known, how can we calculate $P(E \cup F)$ from $P(E)$ and $P(F)$? We find the answer to this question by looking at the Venn diagram for $E \cup F$. (See page 23).

The answer is complicated slightly by the fact that E and F may overlap. To obtain $P(E \cup F)$ we have to add up the probabilities of all the simple events that are in $E \cup F$. We are tempted to try to do this in three steps. First add up the probabilities of the simple events in E. Their sum is $P(E)$. Then add up the probabilities of the simple events in F. Their sum is $P(F)$. Then add the two sums, to get $P(E) + P(F)$. However, this procedure does not give us exactly what we want. When we add the probabilities of the simple events in E, we include the probabilities of those simple events that are in $E \cap F$, the part of E that is also in F. When we add the probabilities of the simple events in F, we include the probabilities of the simple events in $E \cap F$ again. As a result, the probabilities of the simple events in $E \cap F$ are added in twice. To make up for this error we should subtract them once. So it is necessary to add a fourth step to our procedure: Subtract $P(E \cap F)$ from $P(E) + P(F)$. Now we have the correct answer, expressed in the formula

(1) $\qquad P(E \cup F) = P(E) + P(F) - P(E \cap F).$

For example, when a single fair die is tossed, let E be the event that the number that turns up is divisible by 2, and let F be the event that the number that turns up is divisible by 3. The sample space $S = \{1, 2, 3, 4, 5, 6\}$, and the probability of each simple event is $\frac{1}{6}$. $E = \{2, 4, 6\}$, and $P(E) = \frac{3}{6}$. $F = \{3, 6\}$, and $P(F) = \frac{2}{6}$. $E \cap F = \{6\}$, and $P(E \cap F) = \frac{1}{6}$. Then $P(E \cup F) = \frac{3}{6} + \frac{2}{6} - \frac{1}{6} = \frac{4}{6}$. We can verify the result by observing that $E \cup F = \{2, 3, 4, 6\}$ which is the union of four simple events.

Events That Do Not Overlap

Equation (1) takes on a particularly simple form in the special case where the events E and F are mutually exclusive. Then $E \cap F$ is the empty set, and $P(E \cap F) = 0$. Then equation (1) reduces to

(2) $P(E \cup F) = P(E) + P(F)$, $E \cap F = \varnothing$.

If two events E and F are mutually exclusive, the probability that either E or F occurs is the sum of the probabilities of the two events.

To illustrate the use of this rule, let us find the probability that 2 or 3 heads turn up when 4 fair coins are tossed. Let E be the event that exactly 2 heads turn up. Let F be the event that exactly 3 heads turn up. E and F are mutually exclusive. $E \cup F$ is the event that 2 or 3 heads turn up. By the formula developed on page 69, $P(E) = \binom{4}{2} \Big/ 2^4 = \dfrac{6}{16}$, and $P(F) = \binom{4}{3} \Big/ 2^4 = \dfrac{4}{16}$. Then $P(E \cup F) = \dfrac{6}{16} + \dfrac{4}{16} = \dfrac{5}{8}$.

The same procedure can be used to find the probability that, when two fair dice are rolled, the numbers that turn up add up to 7 or 11. Let $S = \{1, 2, 3, 4, 5, 6\}$. The sample space for this experiment is $S \times S$, and the probability of each simple event in it is $\frac{1}{36}$. Let E be the event that the numbers that turn up add up to 7, and let F be the event that the numbers that turn up add up to 11. $E = \{(1, 6), (2, 5), (3, 4), (4, 3), (5, 2), (6, 1)\}$, and $P(E) = \frac{6}{36}$ $F = \{(5, 6), (6, 5)\}$, and $P(F) = \frac{2}{36}$. Since E and F are mutually exclusive, $P(E \cup F) = \frac{6}{36} + \frac{2}{36} = \frac{2}{9}$.

Complementary Events

An important special case of equation (2) arises when $F = E' =$ the event that E does not occur. Then E and F are mutually exclusive, so that equation (2) applies. However, $E \cup F$ is the entire sample space, so that $P(E \cup F) = 1$. Then equation (2) takes the form

(3) $P(E) + P(E') = 1$,   or $P(E) = 1 - P(E')$.

This equation is useful because it is sometimes easier to compute directly the probability that an event does *not* occur than it is to compute directly the probability that it does occur. Then the latter is obtained from the former by using equation (3). For example, suppose three married couples are at a party, and the men draw lots for choosing dancing partners from among their wives. What is the probability of the event E that at least one man has not chosen his wife? If we picture the men as being arranged in a line, we see that the assignment of dancing partners to the men is like arranging the 3 wives in a line. This can be done in $3! = 6$ ways, all of which are equally likely. Let F be the event that exactly 1 man has not chosen his wife. (This turns out to be impossible, so that $P(F) = 0$.) Let G be the event that exactly 2 men have not chosen their wives. Let H be the event that all 3 men have not chosen their wives. Then $E = G \cup H$, and G and H are mutually exclusive. So we can calculate $P(E)$ by first finding $P(G)$ and $P(H)$, and then adding them. It is easier, however, to note that E' is the event that every man has chosen his wife. This can be done in only one way. Therefore $P(E') = \frac{1}{6}$. Consequently $P(E) = 1 - \frac{1}{6} = \frac{5}{6}$.

Many Events, No Two of Which Overlap

Three events E, F, and G in a sample space are said to be *mutually exclusive in pairs* if $E \cap F = \varnothing$, $E \cap G = \varnothing$, and $F \cap G = \varnothing$, that is, *if no two of the three events overlap.* If E, F, and G are mutually exclusive in pairs, we can find $P(E \cup F \cup G)$ by using equation (2) twice. Let $F \cup G = H$. Then $E \cup F \cup G = E \cup H$. Moreover, by one of the distributive laws noted on page 26, $E \cap H = E \cap (F \cup G) = (E \cap F) \cup (E \cap G)$. But $E \cap F = \varnothing$, and $E \cap G = \varnothing$. Hence $E \cap H = \varnothing \cup \varnothing = \varnothing$. Therefore E and H are mutually exclusive, and we may use equation (2) to find $P(E \cup H)$. We get

(4) $$P(E \cup H) = P(E) + P(H).$$

When H is replaced by $F \cup G$, equation (4) becomes

(5) $\qquad P(E \cup F \cup G) = P(E) + P(F \cup G).$

Since $F \cap G = \varnothing$, we may use equation (2) to find $P(F \cup G)$. We get $P(F \cup G) = P(F) + P(G)$. This entitles us to substitute $P(F) + P(G)$ for $P(F \cup G)$ in equation (5). The conclusion is

(6) $\qquad P(E \cup F \cup G) = P(E) + P(F) + P(G).$
When three events are mutually exclusive in pairs, the probability of their union is the sum of their probabilities.

This result can be generalized to apply to any number of events in a sample space. *The n events $E_1, E_2, \ldots, E_n$ are said to be mutually exclusive in pairs if no two of them overlap. If $E_1, E_2, \ldots, E_n$ are mutually exclusive in pairs, then*

(7) $\qquad P(E_1 \cup E_2 \cup \ldots \cup E_n)$

$$= P(E_1) + P(E_2) + \ldots + P(E_n).$$

That is, if n events are mutually exclusive in pairs, the probability of their union is the sum of their probabilities. The proof of equation (7) is carried out by a procedure like the one used to prove equation (6). It consists essentially of a step by step extension of the result, first to the union of 3 events, then to the union of 4 events, and so on, until finally it is extended to the union of n events. At each step of the proof equation (2) is invoked.

The Union of Many Events

Equation (7) is limited in usefulness because of the restriction that no two of the events $E_1, E_2, \ldots, E_n$ should overlap. To get a formula for $P(E_1 \cup E_2 \cup \ldots \cup E_n)$ that applies to any n events without restriction we have to generalize equation (1) rather than equation (2). This can be done by a step-by-step procedure in which equation (1) is used over and over again to extend the result first to the union of 3 events, then to the union of 4 events, and so on. To show how the reasoning goes, and see the form that the result takes, we shall derive the formula for the probability of the union of 3 events. Let E, F, and G be the 3 events, and, as we did before, let $F \cup G = H$. Then $P(E \cup F \cup G) = P(E \cup H)$ and this, according to equation (1), is equal to $P(E) + P(H) - P(E \cap H)$. So, to begin with, we have

(8) $P(E \cup F \cup G) = P(E) + P(H) - P(E \cap H).$

$P(H) = P(F \cup G)$, and this, according to equation (1) is equal to $P(F) + P(G) - P(F \cap G)$. Substituting this last expression for $P(H)$ in equation (8), we get

(9) $P(E \cup F \cup G) = P(E) + P(F)$
$$+ P(G) - P(F \cap G) - P(E \cap H).$$

We have already observed in the preceding section that $E \cap H = E \cap (F \cup G) = (E \cap F) \cup (E \cap G)$. If we write J for $E \cap F$, and K for $E \cap G$, then $E \cap H = J \cup K$, and $P(E \cap H) = P(J \cup K)$. Applying equation (1) once more, we have $P(J \cup K) = P(J) + P(K) - P(J \cap K)$, so the latter expression may be substituted for $P(E \cap H)$ in equation (9). We get as a result,

(10) $P(E \cup F \cup G) = P(E) + P(F) + P(G)$
$$- P(F \cap G) - [P(J) + P(K) - P(J \cap K)].$$

When we remove the brackets around the last 3 terms, this becomes

(11) $P(E \cup F \cup G) = P(E) + P(F) + P(G)$
$$- P(F \cap G) - P(J) - P(K) + P(J \cap K).$$

Now we recall that $J = E \cap F$, and $K = E \cap G$. Then $J \cap K = (E \cap F) \cap (E \cap G)$. Since the operation $\cap$ is associative and commutative, we may drop the parentheses in this last expression, and rearrange the order in which the entries E, F, E, and G are written. Putting the two E entries first, the expression becomes $E \cap E \cap F \cap G$, and this, in turn becomes $E \cap F \cap G$, since $E \cap E = E$. So we may substitute $E \cap F$ for J, $E \cap G$ for K, and $E \cap F \cap G$ for $J \cap K$, in equation (11). The result is

$$(12) \quad P(E \cup F \cup G) = P(E) + P(F) + P(G)$$
$$- P(F \cap G) - P(E \cap F) - P(E \cap G)$$
$$+ P(E \cap F \cap G).$$

Each of the 3 terms on the second line of this equation has -1 as a coefficient. If we factor out this coefficient, the equation takes the form

$$(13) \quad P(E \cup F \cup G) = P(E) + P(F) + P(G)$$
$$- [P(F \cap G) + P(E \cap F) + P(E \cap G)]$$
$$+ P(E \cap F \cap G).$$

If you compare this equation with equation (6), you will see that they differ in that equation (13) has some additional terms that equation (6) does not have. These additional terms are made necessary by the fact that E, F, and G may overlap. If we return to the restrictive assumption that E, F, and G are mutually exclusive in pairs, then these additional terms become equal to zero, and equation (13) reduces to equation (6).

In order to see how equation (13) may be extended to the union of 4 or more events, we shall first observe the nature of the terms that appear on the right-hand side of the equation, and then write them in abbreviated form. From among the events E, F, and G, take *one event at a time*, in all possible ways, find the probability of each event, and then add these probabilities. The result is the sum $P(E) + P(F) + P(G)$, which appears on the first line of equation (13). Call this sum S_1. From among the events E, F, and G, *take two events at a time*, in all possible ways. Write the intersection of each pair, then find the probability of each intersection, and add these probabilities. The result is the sum $P(F \cap G) + P(E \cap F) + P(E \cap G)$, which appears on the second line of equation (13). Call this sum S_2. From among the events E, F, and G, *take three events at a time*, in all possible ways. Write the intersection of each triple, then find the probability of each intersection, and add these probabilities. The result is $P(E \cap F \cap G)$, which appears on the third line of equation (13). Call this sum S_3. The equation (13) can be written in the abbreviated form

(14) $\qquad P(E \cup F \cup G) = S_1 - S_2 + S_3.$

Equation (14) suggests the form that a generalization of the formula will take. We state the conclusion now, without going into the details of the proof. The proof is essentially a step by step extension of equation (14), first to the union of 4 events, then to the union of 5 events, and so on, until finally it is extended to the union of n events. At each step of the proof equation (1) is invoked. The conclusion is: *Let $E_1, E_2, \ldots, E_n$ be any n events in a sample space. Let S_1 be the sum of the probabilities of the events taken one at a time. Let S_2 be the sum of the probabilities of the intersections of the events taken two at a time. Let S_3 be the sum of the probabilities of the intersections of the events taken three at a time. $S_4, \ldots, S_n$ are defined similarly. Then,*

(15) $\qquad P(E_1 \cup E_2 \cup \ldots \cup E_n) = S_1 - S_2 + S_3$
$$- S_4 + \ldots \pm S_n,$$

where the signs on the right hand side alternate between $+$ and $-$. The sign of S_n will be $+$ or $-$ depending on whether n is odd or even.

The Careless Cloak-room Attendant

The men at a theatrical performance checked their hats at the cloak-room. After the performance, the cloak-room attendant, who was in a hurry to get home, simply handed out the hats at random. If n is the number of men who checked their hats, what is the probability that at least one man got his own hat back? We shall answer this question with the help of equation (15).

It is convenient for us to designate the men by numbers, from 1 to n, and to number the hats, too, by assigning each man's number to his hat. After the hats are handed out, let us imagine the men arranged in line in numerical order. Then the arrangement of the hats will be a permutation of the numbers from 1 to n. Every possible way of handing out the hats corresponds to one such permutation, and vice versa. So we may choose as sample space the set S of all possible permutations of the n numbered hats. Then $n(S) = n!$. We shall assume that all permutations are equally likely, so the probability of each permutation is $1/n!$. Let E_1 be the event that man number 1 got his own hat back. Let E_2 be the event that man number 2 got his own hat back. Define $E_3, \ldots, E_n$ in a similar manner. Then the event that at least one man got his own hat back is $E_1 \cup E_2 \cup \ldots \cup E_n$. The probability we are trying to find is $P(E_1 \cup E_2 \cup \ldots \cup E_n)$, and this can be computed by using equation (15). But first we must find the values of $S_1, S_2, \ldots, S_n$. To calculate S_1, we find $P(E_j)$ for all values of j from 1 to n, and then add these probabilities. E_j is the event that man j has hat j. This event occurs when hat j is given to man j, and the other hats are handed out in any order whatever. Since there are $n - 1$ other hats to hand out, and they can be handed out in $(n - 1)!$ ways, E_j consists of $(n - 1)!$ elements of S, and therefore $P(E_j) = (n - 1)!/n!$. The factors of the numerator in this fraction cancel all factors except n in the denominator, so $P(E_j) = 1/n$ for all values of j. Then $S_1 = \dfrac{1}{n} + \dfrac{1}{n} + \ldots + \dfrac{1}{n} = 1$, since there are n terms in the sum. To calculate S_2, we find $P(E_j \cap E_k)$ for all two-number subsets, $\{j, k\}$, selected from the set

$\{1, 2, \ldots, n\}$, and then add these probabilities. The event $E_j \cap E_k$ occurs when man j and man k are given their own hats, and the remaining $n - 2$ hats are handed out in any order. This can be done in $(n - 2)!$ ways, so $P(E_j \cap E_k) = (n - 2)/n! = 1/n(n - 1)$ since all factors from 1 up to $n - 2$ occur in both numerator and denominator and may be canceled. The number of two-number subsets $\{j, k\}$ that may be selected from $\{1, 2, \ldots, n\}$ is $\binom{n}{2} = \dfrac{n(n - 1)}{1 \times 2}$. Then S_2 is the sum of $\dfrac{n(n - 1)}{2!}$ terms all of which are equal to $1/n(n - 1)$. Therefore $S_2 = \dfrac{1}{2!}$. By similar reasoning, we find that for any 3-number subset $\{j, k, m\}$ selected from $\{1, 2, \ldots, n\}$, $P(E_j \cap E_k \cap E_m = (n - 3)!/n! = 1/n(n - 1)(n - 2)$, and there are $\binom{n}{3} = \dfrac{n(n - 1)(n - 2)}{1 \times 2 \times 3}$ such terms to be added to obtain S_3. Therefore $S_3 = \dfrac{1}{3!}$. In the same way, $S_4 = \dfrac{1}{4!}$, and so on, up to $S_n = \dfrac{1}{n!}$. Consequently, by equation (15),

$$P(E_1 \cup E_2 \cup \ldots \cup E_n) = 1 - \frac{1}{2!} + \frac{1}{3!} - \cdots \cdots \pm \frac{1}{n!}.$$

If $n = 1$, this probability is 1. If $n = 2$, this probability is $\frac{1}{2}$. If we use the abbreviated notation P for $P(E_1 \cup E_2 \cup \ldots \cup E_n)$, its values for higher values of n are shown in this table, computed to five decimal places:

n	3	4	5	6	7
P	.66667	.62500	.63333	.63196	.63214

Notice the surprising result that, if there are more than two men checking their hats, the probability that at least one man gets his own hat back is approximately $\frac{2}{3}$ no matter how large the value of n is! This result can be reformulated in an interesting way with the help of the infinite series for e^{-1} given on page 86. We saw that $e^{-1} = \frac{1}{2!} - \frac{1}{3!} + \ldots$. If we subtract e^{-1} from 1, we get $1 - e^{-1} = 1 - \frac{1}{2!} + \frac{1}{3!} - \ldots$. Notice that P is simply the sum of the first n terms of this series. Consequently, the values of P for larger and larger values of n are better and better approximations of the number $1 - e^{-1}$. Here we are interested in using this fact backwards: *The number $1 - e^{-1}$ is an approximation of the probability P that at least one of the n men gets his own hat back, when the hats are returned at random.* The number $1 - e^{-1} = .63212 \ldots$, so we see that the approximation is a good one for values of n that are greater than 2.

The hat problem is one of many versions of the famous problem of *rencontre*, or *matching*, first discussed by the French mathematician Montmort in 1708. Montmort presented the problem in this form: Thirteen cards numbered from 1 to 13 are put into a bag, and then are drawn out at random, one at a time. What is the probability that the number on at least one card matches the number of the order in which it was drawn? This is like the hat problem with $n = 13$. Another common formulation of the problem is this: A secretary has typed the envelopes for n letters, but she puts the letters into the envelopes at random. What is the probability that at least one letter is put into the right envelope? This is like the hat problem, with envelopes substituted for the men, and letters substituted for the hats.

Conditional Probability

A survey of the heads of ten households in a suburban street obtained the answers to three questions: Do you

have a telephone? Are you a Republican or a Democrat?
Is your income over $7,000 per year? The answers to the
questions are recorded in the table below, where the householders are designated by numbers from 1 to 10. If one
of the ten householders is chosen at random, what is the
probability that he is a Republican? To answer this question, we may choose as sample space S the set of all ten
householders, and assign probability .1 to each of its
simple events. Let E be the event that the householder
chosen is a Republican. Then $n(E) = 4$, and $n(S) = 10$,
so $P(E) = n(E)/n(S) = .4$.

Householder	Telephone	Politics	Income over $7,000
1	yes	D	yes
2	no	D	no
3	yes	R	yes
4	yes	D	no
5	yes	R	yes
6	no	D	no
7	yes	R	yes
8	yes	D	no
9	no	R	no
10	no	D	no

In the diagram below, the sample space S is represented
by a set of ten squares. The shaded squares represent the
householders who have a telephone. The political affilia-

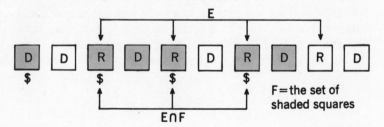

tion of each householder is indicated in the squares. A
dollar sign under a square indicates an income over $7,000.
The upper arrows indicate the elements of E.

We now modify the question somewhat in this way.
Suppose you choose one of the householders at random,
ring his doorbell, and observe when the door is opened
that there is a telephone in the house. What is the probability that the householder is a Republican? The observed
fact that the householder has a telephone changes the
conditions of the problem. It shows immediately that the
householder whose doorbell you have rung cannot be
householder number 2, 6, 9 or 10. Since these are no longer
possible outcomes of the experiment, we exclude them
from the sample space. Let F be the event that a householder in S has a telephone. The reduced sample space is F,
and is indicated by the shaded squares in the diagram
on page 105.

The only members of E we have to consider now are
those that are in F. The set of elements of E that are in F
is $E \cap F$. The lower arrows in the diagram indicate the
elements of $E \cap F$. Under these conditions, the probability that the householder is a Republican is $n(E \cap F)/n(F)$
$= \frac{3}{6} = .5$. This is not the same result that we got before.
To distinguish it from the earlier probability, we call it
the *conditional probability of E given F*, and we designate
it by the symbol $P(E \mid F)$. It is called a *conditional probability* because it is the probability that E occurs on the
condition that F also occurs.

Strictly speaking, $P(E \mid F)$ is the probability of an event
in the reduced sample space F. However, it is possible to
calculate it from the probabilities of events in the original
sample space S. To get a formula for this purpose, take
the fraction $n(E \cap F)/n(F)$, that we used above, and
divide the numerator and denominator by $n(S)$. Then we
get

$$\frac{n(E \cap F)/n(S)}{n(F)/n(S)} = \frac{P(E \cap F)}{P(F)}$$

The numerator and denominator of the fraction on the left signify probabilities only in a sample space S whose simple events are all equally likely. The numerator and denominator of the fraction on the right, however, can signify probabilities even if the simple events in S are not all equally likely. In order to make the concept of conditional probability applicable to *all* sample spaces, we define it as follows: If E and F are events in a sample space S, and $P(F) \neq 0$,

(16) $$P(E \mid F) = P(E \cap F)/P(F).$$

The restriction that $P(F)$ is not 0 is necessary in order to avoid having 0 in the denominator of a fraction.

For further examples of the use of this formula, let E and F be the events defined above in the sample space S of ten householders. Let G be the event that a householder has an income above \$7,000 a year. Then

$$P(G \mid F) = \frac{P(G \cap F)}{P(F)} = \frac{.4}{.6} = \frac{2}{3} = .67 \text{ approximately,}$$

and

$$P(E \mid G) = \frac{P(E \cap G)}{P(G)} = \frac{.3}{.4} = .75.$$

The Intersection of Two Events

We can derive from equation (16) a useful formula for the probability of the intersection of two events. Multiply both sides of the equation by $P(F)$. Then we get

(17) $$P(E \cap F) = P(F)P(E \mid F).$$

If $P(E) \neq 0$, F and E may be interchanged in this formula. Then we get $P(F \cap E) = P(E)P(F \mid E)$. Since $F \cap E = E \cap F$, this gives us another formula for $P(E \cap F)$:

(18) $$P(E \cap F) = P(E)P(F \mid E).$$

These formulas are often used for calculating probabilities in a compound experiment without constructing the sample space for the experiment. For example, suppose a class of 30 children contains 12 boys and 18 girls. Suppose 4 of the boys and 9 of the girls are on the honor roll. The teacher chooses a child in the class at random to serve as monitor. What is the probability that the monitor is a boy on the honor roll? What is the probability that the monitor is a girl on the honor roll? What is the probability that the monitor is on the honor roll? To answer these questions, think of the experiment of choosing a monitor as a compound experiment made up of two steps. Step 1, choose one of the two sexes. Step two, choose one of the children of that sex. Let B be the event that the monitor chosen is a boy. Let G be the event that the monitor chosen is a girl. Let H be the event that the monitor chosen is on the honor roll. Then $B \cap H$ is the event that the monitor is a boy on the honor roll. Applying formula (18), we have $P(B \cap H) = P(B)P(H \mid B)$. $P(B)$, the probability of choosing a boy, is $\frac{2}{5}$. $P(H \mid B)$, the conditional probability that the monitor is on the honor roll, given that he is a boy, is $\frac{1}{3}$. So $P(B \cap H) = \frac{2}{5} \times \frac{1}{3} = \frac{2}{15}$ (See the tree diagram below.) Similarly, $P(G \cap H) = P(G)P(H \mid G)$. $P(G) = \frac{3}{5}$, and $P(H \mid G) = \frac{1}{2}$. $G \cap H$ is the event that the monitor is a girl on the honor roll, and $P(G \cap H) = \frac{3}{5} \times \frac{1}{2} = \frac{3}{10}$. H, the event that the monitor

$$P(H \mid B) = \tfrac{1}{3}$$
$$P(B) = .4$$
$$P(H' \mid B) = \tfrac{2}{3}$$
$$P(H \mid G) = \tfrac{1}{2}$$
$$P(G) = .6$$
$$P(H' \mid G) = \tfrac{1}{2}$$

$$P(B \cap H) = P(B) \times P(H \mid B) = .4 \times \tfrac{1}{3}$$
$$P(B \cap H') = P(B) \times P(H' \mid B) = .4 \times \tfrac{2}{3}$$
$$P(G \cap H) = P(G) \times P(H \mid G) = .6 \times \tfrac{1}{2}$$
$$P(G \cap H') = P(G) \times P(H' \mid G) = .6 \times \tfrac{1}{2}$$

Tree diagram illustrating use of conditional probabilities

is on the honor roll, is the union of the mutually exclusive events $B \cap H$ and $G \cap H$, so $P(H) = P(B \cap H) + P(G \cap H) = \frac{2}{15} + \frac{3}{10} = \frac{13}{30}$. All three answers can be verified by using the class of 30 children as a sample space S in which all possible outcomes of choosing a monitor are equally likely.

How Evidence Modifies Beliefs

Let us consider again the class used in the example above. Suppose the principal of the school sends the teacher a note saying "Please send me one of your pupils as a monitor at dismissal time." After dispatching the message, the principal muses, "I wonder if she will send me a boy?" He looks up the class register, and assuming that the monitor is chosen at random, he concludes that the probability of his being sent a boy, $P(B)$, is $\frac{2}{5}$. Five minutes later the principal receives a note from the teacher saying, "I shall send you someone who is on the honor roll." With this new information in hand, that the monitor chosen is on the honor roll, the principal can now make a better estimate of the probability that the monitor is a boy by calculating $P(B \mid H)$, the conditional probability that the monitor is a boy, given that he or she is on the honor roll. We shall derive a formula for $P(B \mid H)$ with the help of equations (16), (17) and (18). In this context, $P(B)$ is called the *a priori* probability of B, while $P(B \mid H)$ is called *a posteriori* probability of B, since they are calculated *before* and *after* the principal had the information revealed in the teacher's note.

We observe first that the events B and G defined in the sample space S for this problem have these properties: $P(B) \neq 0$, $P(G) \neq 0$, $B \cap G = \varnothing$, and $B \cup G = S$. The first two properties assure us that $P(H \mid B)$ and $P(H \mid G)$ exist, as defined by equation (16). The last two properties say that the set of boys and the set of girls in the class do not overlap, and together they make up the entire class.

This division of the class by sex also cuts across the set of honor students, H, and divides it into two mutually exclusive sets, $H \cap B$ and $H \cap G$ whose union is H. Then, by equation (2), $P(H) = P(H \cap B) + P(H \cap G)$. We get substitutes for the last two terms by using equation (17):

$$P(H \cap B) = P(B)P(H \mid B), \text{ and } P(H \cap G) = P(G)P(H \mid G).$$

Making these substitutions, we find

$$(19) \qquad P(H) = P(B)P(H \mid B) + P(G)P(H \mid G).$$

This is the formula we used in effect in the preceding section when we calculated $P(H)$. We write it out explicitly now because we shall need it.

From equation (16) we know that $P(B \mid H) = \dfrac{P(B \cap H)}{P(H)}$. Equation (18) tells us that we may replace $P(B \cap H)$ by $P(B)P(H \mid B)$. Equation (19) gives us a substitute for $P(H)$. Making these substitutions in the numerator and the denominator of the fraction, we find that

$$(20) \quad P(B \mid H) = \frac{P(B)P(H \mid B)}{P(B)P(H \mid B) + P(G)P(H \mid G)}.$$

From the data given to us about the class, $P(B) = \frac{2}{5}$, $P(G) = \frac{3}{5}$, $P(H \mid B) = \frac{1}{3}$, and $P(H \mid G) = \frac{1}{2}$. Substituting these numbers in equation (20), we find that $P(B \mid H) = \frac{4}{13}$. Notice that this *a posteriori* probability is lower than the *a priori* probability, which was $\frac{2}{5}$. The information in the teacher's note to the principal has compelled him to revise downwards his estimate of the probability that the monitor will be a boy.

Beating the Weatherman At His Own Game

Equation (20) can be generalized as follows: Let E_1, $E_2, \ldots, E_n$ be events in a sample space S that have the properties that they are mutually exclusive in pairs, their union is the entire space S, and the probability of each of them is not 0. Let E be an event in S whose probability is not 0. Then

(21) $\qquad P(E_k \mid E) =$

$$\frac{P(E_k)P(E \mid E_k)}{P(E_1)P(E \mid E_1) + P(E_2)P(E \mid E_2) + \ldots + P(E_n)P(E \mid E_n)},$$

for all values of k from 1 to n. This equation is known as Bayes's Theorem, after Thomas Bayes, who first used it during the eighteenth century. In applications of Bayes's Theorem it is customary to refer to the events E_k as *hypotheses*. $P(E_k)$ is the *a priori* probability that the hypothesis E_k is true. $P(E_k \mid E)$ is the *a posteriori* probability that the hypothesis E_k is true, based on the fact that the event E occurs.

To give another example of the use of Bayes's Theorem we now consider a little problem in weather forecasting, from the layman's point of view. Suppose that long experience in a certain region shows that, on the average, each year it rains on 70 days, snows on 30 days, is cloudy on 130 days, and is fair on 135 days. In the absence of any other weather information, we might assume that tomorrow's weather has the following *a priori* probabilities: If E_1, E_2, E_3, and E_4 are the events rain, snow, cloudiness, and fair weather respectively, then $P(E_1) = \frac{70}{365} = .19$, $P(E_2) = \frac{30}{365} = .08$, $P(E_3) = \frac{130}{365} = .36$, and $P(E_4) = \frac{135}{365} = .37$, approximately. However, we do have other weather information in the form of the weatherman's forecast. But we cannot take the weatherman at his word, because he is sometimes wrong. Suppose we have been checking the accuracy of the weatherman's forecasts for a long period of time, and have come up with the following data:

For every 10 days of rain, the weatherman had forecast *rain* 9 times, and *cloudy weather* 1 time. For every 10 days of snow, the weatherman had forecast *snow* 8 times, *cloudy weather* 1 time, and *fair weather* 1 time. For every 10 days of cloudy weather, the weatherman had forecast *cloudy weather* 6 times, *rain* 2 times, *snow* 1 time, and *fair weather* 1 time. For every 10 days of fair weather, the weatherman had forecast *fair weather* 7 times, *rain* 1 time, *snow* 1 time, and *cloudy weather* 1 time.

This information permits us to form new judgments about the weather based on the weatherman's forecast and our estimate of the degree of accuracy of the weatherman's forecast. In this way we beat the weatherman at his own game. Suppose, for example, that the weatherman forecasts that tomorrow's weather will be fair. Call this fair weather forecast E. Then we can calculate $P(E_4 \mid E)$, the conditional probability that tomorrow will be fair, given that the weatherman says it will be, by using Bayes' Theorem. Our check on the weatherman shows that $P(E \mid E_1) = 0$, $P(E \mid E_2) = .1$, $P(E \mid E_3) = .1$, and $P(E \mid E_4) = .7$. Then

$$P(E_4 \mid E)$$

$$= \frac{P(E_4)P(E \mid E_4)}{P(E_1)P(E \mid E_1) + P(E_2)P(E \mid E_2) + P(E_3)P(E \mid E_3) + P(E_4)P(E \mid E_4)}$$

$$= \frac{.37 \times .7}{(.19 \times 0) + (.08 \times .1) + (.36 \times .1) + (.37 \times .7)}$$

$$= \frac{.259}{.008 + .036 + .259} = \frac{.259}{.303} = .85.$$

We conclude, then, that when this particular weatherman predicts fair weather, the probability of having fair weather is 85%.

Independent Events

Suppose that a tray is divided by a partition into two compartments, and that there are 7 white balls and 7 black balls distributed between the two compartments as shown in the diagram. Consider the experiment of drawing a ball at random from the tray. Use as a sample space the set

$$S = \{w_1, w_2, w_3, w_4, w_5, w_6, w_7, b_1, b_2, b_3, b_4, b_5, b_6, b_7\}.$$

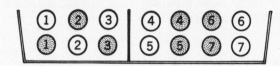

Let E be the event that the ball drawn is white. Let F be the event that the ball drawn is in the left-hand compartment. $E \cap F$ is the event that the ball drawn is white and is in the left-hand compartment.

$$E = \{w_1, w_2, w_3, w_4, w_5, w_6, w_7\},$$

and $P(E) = \frac{1}{2}$. $F = \{w_1, w_2, w_3, b_1, b_2, b_3\}$, and $P(F) = \frac{3}{7}$. $E \cap F = \{w_1, w_2, w_3\}$, and $P(E \cap F) = \frac{3}{14}$. Let us find the conditional probability that the ball drawn is white, given that it is in the left-hand compartment. Using equation (16), we have $P(E \mid F) = P(E \cap F)/P(F) = \dfrac{3/14}{3/7} = \frac{1}{2}$. This result is also evident in the diagram, since there are 3 white balls out of 6 in the reduced sample space F. Notice that in this case $P(E \mid F) = P(E)$, that is, the probability of E is the same *with* or *without* the condition that F occurs. We use this relationship as the foundation for an important concept: If E and F are events in a sample space S, and $P(E \mid F) = P(E)$, we say that E is *independent of F*.

If both $P(E)$ and $P(F)$ are not 0, E and F may be interchanged in equation (16). Then equations (17) and (18) are both valid, and give us two expressions for $P(E \cap F)$. Equating these two expressions, we get $P(E)P(F \mid E) = P(F)P(E \mid F)$. Now suppose E is independent of F. Then $P(E \mid F) = P(E)$, and $P(E)$ may be substituted for $P(E \mid F)$. Then we have $P(E)P(F \mid E) = P(F)P(E)$. Since $P(E) \neq 0$, we may divide by it, and we find that $P(F \mid E) = P(F)$, that is, that F *is independent* of E. We have proved, then, that *when $P(E)$ and $P(F)$ are not 0, if*

E is independent of F, then F is independent of E. When *E* is independent of *F*, equation (17) can be rewritten with $P(E)$ substituted for $P(E \mid F)$. Then it takes the form

$$(22) \qquad P(E \cap F) = P(E)P(F).$$

We use equation (22) as the basis for a new definition. We say that two events *E* and *F* are *independent* if equation (22) holds. This equation is called the multiplication rule for two independent events.

The reader may wonder why we did not use the condition $P(E \mid F) = P(E)$ to define the relation "*E* and *F* are independent." The reason is that it is meaningful only when $P(F) \neq 0$, since this assumption is part of the definition of $P(E \mid F)$. Equation (22) has meaning, however, even if $P(E)$ or $P(F) = 0$. So, by basing the concept of independence of events on equation (22), we make it more widely applicable. If *E* is independent of *F*, then *E* and *F* are independent. But if *E* and *F* are independent, *E* is independent of *F* only if $P(F) \neq 0$.

Intuition Is Unreliable

In some experiments we have an intuitive feeling that certain events are independent. For example, when two fair dice are thrown, it seems reasonable to believe that the way one die turns up is not influenced at all by the way the other die turns up. So we would guess that if *E* is the event that the first die turns up a 1, and *F* is the event that the second die turns up a 3, then *E* and *F* are independent. We can check this guess easily. $E = \{(1, 1), (1, 2), (1, 3), (1, 4), (1,5), (1, 6)\}$, and $P(E) = \frac{1}{6}$. $F = \{(1, 3), (2, 3), (3, 3), (4, 3), (5, 3), (6, 3)\}$, and $P(F) = \frac{1}{6}$. $E \cap F = \{(1, 3)\}$, and $P(E \cap F) = \frac{1}{36}$. Consequently $P(E \cap F) = P(E)P(F)$, and *E* and *F* are independent.

However, here is a situation where intuition doesn't help very much. For families with a given number of children, assume that all possible distributions of sex are equally likely. For a family of two children, there would be four equally likely possibilities, *bb*, *bg*, *gb*, and *gg*. Similarly, for a family with 3 children there would be 8 equally likely possibilities, and for a family with 4 children there would be 16 equally likely possibilities. Restricting our attention to families of one size only, let *E* be the event that the family has children of both sexes, and let *F* be the event that there is at most one girl in the family. Are the events *E* and *F* independent? Try to answer this question intuitively before you read any further, and then compare your intuitive answer with the answer we get in the next paragraphs by using equation (22) as the criterion for independence.

Consider first the case where there are 2 children in a family. The sample space of possible distributions of sex has 4 elements, and the probability of each simple event is $\frac{1}{4}$. $E = \{bg, gb\}$, and $P(E) = \frac{1}{2}$. $F = \{bb, bg, gb\}$, and $P(F) = \frac{3}{4}$. $E \cap F = E$, so $P(E \cap F) = \frac{1}{2}$. Consequently $P(E \cap F) \neq P(E)P(F)$, and *E* and *F* are *not independent*.

Consider next the case where there are 3 children in a family. The sample space of possible distributions of sex has 8 elements, and the probability of each simple event is $\frac{1}{8}$. Instead of enumerating the elements of *E*, *F*, and $E \cap F$, let us take advantage of the fact that listing possible distributions of sex among three children is like getting all possible outcomes when three coins are tossed, since the choice *b* or *g* for a child is like the choice *H* or *T* for a coin. Then the expansion of $(b + g)^3$ by the binomial theorem can help us find the information we want: $(b + g)^3 = 1b^3 + 3b^2g + 3bg^2 + 1g^3$. The second and third term of the expansion corresponds to the elements of *E*. So $n(E) = 3 + 3 = 6$, and $P(E) = \frac{6}{8}$. The first two terms of the expansion correspond to the elements of *F*. So $n(F) = 1 + 3 = 4$, and $P(F) = \frac{4}{8}$. The second term alone corresponds to $E \cap F$, so $n(E \cap F) = 3$, and $P(E \cap F) = \frac{3}{8}$. In this case $P(E \cap F) = P(E)P(F)$, and *E* and *F* are *independent*. So we have the strange result that, although the events E and F are defined in the same words for both cases, they are independent for families with 3 children, but are not independent for families with 2 children.

The moral of this example is, don't rely on intuition to determine if two events are independent. Test them for independence by seeing if they satisfy equation (22).

Independence of More Than Two Events

There is an analogy between equation (22) and equation (2) that becomes evident when we write them under each other:

(2) $P(E \cup F) = P(E) + P(F)$, when E and F are mutually exclusive.

(22) $P(E \cap F) = P(E) \times P(F)$, when E and F are independent.

Equation (2) becomes equation (22) if we replace $\cup$ by $\cap$, $+$ by $\times$, and *mutually exclusive* by *independent*. This analogy tempts us to try to get a generalization of equation (22) by getting the analog of the generalization of equation (2). The generalization of equation (2) is equation (7): $P(E_1 \cup E_2 \cup \ldots \cup E_n) = P(E_1) + P(E_2) + \ldots + P(E_n)$, if $E_1, E_2, \ldots, E_n$ are mutually exclusive in pairs. The analog of this statement would be the assertion that $P(E_1 \cap E_2 \cap \ldots \cap E_n) = P(E_1)P(E_2) \ldots P(E_n)$ if $E_1, E_2, \ldots, E_n$ are independent in pairs. Unfortunately, *this assertion is not true*, as we may see in the following example: Let a green and a red die be rolled. Use as sample space $S \times S$, where $S = \{1, 2, 3, 4, 5, 6\}$. Let E_1 be the event that the green die turns up 4. Let E_2 be the event that the red die turns up 2. Let E_3 be the event that the sum of the numbers turned up by both dice is odd. $E_1 = \{(4, 1), (4, 2), (4, 3), (4, 4), (4, 5), (4, 6)\}$, and $P(E_1) = \frac{1}{6}$. $E_2 = \{(1, 2), (2, 2), (3, 2), (4, 2), (5, 2), (6, 2)\}$, and

$P(E_2) = \frac{1}{6}$. Inspection of the elements of $S \times S$ shows that half of them have odd sums, so that $P(E_3) = \frac{1}{2}$. $E_1 \cap E_2 = \{(4, 2)\}$, so that $P(E_1 \cap E_2) = \frac{1}{36}$. $E_1 \cap E_3 = \{(4, 1), (4, 3), (4, 5)\}$, so that $P(E_1 \cap E_3) = \frac{1}{12}$. $E_2 \cap E_3 = \{(1, 2), (3, 2), (5, 2)\}$, so that $P(E_2 \cap E_3) = \frac{1}{12}$. Then $P(E_1 \cap E_2) = P(E_1)P(E_2)$, $P(E_1 \cap E_3) = P(E_1)P(E_3)$, and $P(E_2 \cap E_3) = P(E_2)P(E_3)$, so that E_1, E_2, and E_3 are independent in pairs. Nevertheless, $P(E_1 \cap E_2 \cap E_3) \neq P(E_1)P(E_2)P(E_3)$, since $E_1 \cap E_2 \cap E_3 = \varnothing$, so that $P(E_1 \cap E_2 \cap E_3) = 0$, while $P(E_1)P(E_2)P(E_3) = \frac{1}{72}$.

The example we have just seen shows that if three events are independent in pairs, there is no guarantee that the intersection of the three events will obey a multiplication rule that states that the probability of the intersection is the product of the probabilities. If we want a generalization of the concept of independent events to assure the existence of such a multiplication rule, we must include the rule as part of the generalized definition. That is why the independence of 3 events is defined as follows: Three events E_1, E_2, and E_3 are called *independent*, if they satisfy the following multiplication rules:

$P(E_1 \cap E_2) = P(E_1)P(E_2)$, $P(E_1 \cap E_3) = P(E_1)P(E_3)$, $P(E_2 \cap E_3) = P(E_2)P(E_3)$, and $P(E_1 \cap E_2 \cap E_3) = P(E_1)P(E_2)P(E_3)$.

We define independence of n events in a similar manner: *The events $E_1, E_2, \ldots, E_n$ are called independent if every subset of two or more of these events satisfies a multiplication rule, that is, the probability of the intersection of the events in the subset is the product of their probabilities.*

Independent Experiments

We have an intuitive notion of what is meant by *independence* of two experiments. However, since intuition is not always a reliable guide, we had better not lean on it too much. We shall use it only long enough to suggest how a precise definition of the concept of independent experiments can be derived from the concept of independent events.

Suppose we perform two experiments in succession as follows: First we toss a tack, with possible outcomes designated by the sample space $S = \{U, D\}$, whose simple events have the probabilities $P(\{U\}) = p$, $P(\{D\}) = q$. Then we toss a coin (which may be unfair), with possible outcomes designated by the sample space $R = \{H, T\}$, whose simple events have the probabilities $P(\{H\}) = r$, $P(\{T\}) = s$. The sample space of the compound experiment is $S \times R = \{(U, H), (U, T), (D, H), (D, T)\}$. How shall we assign probabilities to the simple events in this product space to get a probability model that will fit our intuitive notions that the two experiments are independent?

Let $P(\{(U, H)\}) = a$, $P(\{(U, T)\}) = b$, $P(\{(D, H)\}) = c$, and $P(\{(D, T)\}) = d$. Our problem is to relate a, b, c, and d to p, q, r, and s in a way that conforms to our intuitive notion of what the consequences should be if the two experiments are independent. Let E_1 be the event in $S \times R$ that the tack falls *point up*. $E_1 = \{(U, H), (U, T)\}$. It seems reasonable to assume that if the two experiments are independent, the probability of the tack's falling point up is the same whether we toss the coin or not. If we toss the tack alone, $P(\{U\}) = p$. So our intuition leads us to assume that if the experiments are independent $P(E_1) = p$. Let E_2 be the event in $S \times R$ that the tack falls *point down*. $E_2 = \{(D, H), (D, T)\}$. Intuitively we expect $P(E_2) = q$. Let E_3 be the event that the coin falls *heads*. $E_3 = \{(U, H), (D, H)\}$, and we expect that $P(E_3) = r$. Let E_4 be the event that the coin falls tails. $E_4 = \{(U, T), (D, T)\}$, and we expect that $P(E_4) = s$. If the experiments are independent, we would expect the events, "the tack falls point up," and "the coin falls heads" to be independent. This would mean that $P(E_1 \cap E_3) = P(E_1)P(E_3)$. But $E_1 \cap E_3 = \{(U, H)\}$, and $P(\{(U, H)\}) =$

a, while we expect $P(E_1)P(E_3) = pr$. Consequently, our intuition leads us to the conclusion that $a = pr$. Similarly, we expect E_1 and E_4 to be independent. This leads to the conclusion that $b = ps$. We also expect E_2 and E_3 to be independent, and E_2 and E_4 to be independent. These assumptions lead to the conclusion that $c = qr$ and $d = qs$. The four equations $a = pr$, $b = ps$, $c = qr$, and $d = qs$ tell us how to define the probabilities for a product space associated with a compound experiment made up of independent experiments: *Given two experiments with sample spaces S and R respectively, and each with a suitable assignment of probabilities for its simple events. If the two experiments are performed in succession, we say that the experiments are independent if, for each element (x, y) in $S \times R$, $P(\{(x, y)\}) = P(\{x\})P(\{y\})$.* This definition is

$P(\{U\}) = p$

$P(\{H\}) = r$ $P(\{(U, H)\}) = pr$

$P(\{T\}) = s$ $P(\{(U, T)\}) = ps$

$P(\{D\}) = q$

$P(\{H\}) = r$ $P(\{(D, H)\}) = qr$

$P(\{T\}) = s$ $P(\{(D, T)\}) = qs$

Assignment of probabilities to possible outcomes of a compound experiment made up of two independent experiments, tossing a tack and tossing a coin

easily extended to a compound experiment made up of n separate experiments. *We say that the n experiments are independent if, for each possible outcome $(x_1, x_2, \ldots, x_n)$ of the compound experiment, $P(\{(x_1, x_2, \ldots, x_n)\}) = P(\{x_1\})P(\{x_2\}) \ldots P(\{x_n\})$.* Thus there is a multiplication rule for calculating the probability of the simple events when a compound experiment is made up of a sequence of independent experiments.

As a specific example, consider the compound experiment of tossing a fair coin and rolling a fair die. Let $S = \{H, T\}$, and let $R = \{1, 2, 3, 4, 5, 6\}$. The probability of each simple event is S is $\frac{1}{2}$. The probability of each simple event in R is $\frac{1}{6}$. If the two experiments are independent, we assign to each simple event of $S \times R$ the probability of $\frac{1}{2} \times \frac{1}{6} = \frac{1}{12}$. It is easy to verify that all the requirements for a probability model are satisfied by this assignment.

Independent Trials

The multiplication rule for independent experiments enables us to construct probability models for compound experiments made up of repeated trials of a single experiment, where the trials are assumed to be independent. Repeated tossings of a coin or of a tack are examples of such independent trials.

If a fair coin is tossed once, the sample space is $S = \{H, T\}$, and the probability of each possible outcome is $\frac{1}{2}$. If the coin is tossed 3 times the sample space for the compound experiment is $S \times S \times S$. If the tosses are independent, the probability of each simple event in $S \times S \times S$ is $\frac{1}{2} \times \frac{1}{2} \times \frac{1}{2} = (\frac{1}{2})^3$. If the coin is tossed n times, the sample space for the compound experiment is $S_1 \times S_2 \times S_n$, where each $S_i = S$, for $i = 1, 2, \ldots, n$. If the tosses are independent, the probability of each simple event in $S_1 \times S_2 \times \ldots \times S_n$ is $\frac{1}{2} \times \frac{1}{2} \times \ldots \times \frac{1}{2}$, with $\frac{1}{2}$ used as a factor n times, so that the product is $(\frac{1}{2})^n$. This is equivalent to the assignment of probabilities we have already been making on the assumption that the 2^n possible outcomes are equally likely.

If a tack is tossed once, the sample space is $T = \{U, D\}$. Let $P(\{U\}) = p$, and $P(\{D\}) = q$, where $p + q = 1$. If the tack is tossed 3 times, the sample space for the compound experiment is $T \times T \times T$. If the tosses are independent, the probability of each simple event in $T \times T \times$

T is computed by means of the multiplication rule for independent experiments, as shown in the table below:

Simple Event	Probability	Simple Event	Probability
$\{UUU\}$	$p \times p \times p = p^3$	$\{UDD\}$	$p \times q \times q = pq^2$
$\{UUD\}$	$p \times p \times q = p^2q$	$\{DUD\}$	$q \times p \times q = pq^2$
$\{UDU\}$	$p \times q \times p = p^2q$	$\{DDU\}$	$q \times q \times p = pq^2$
$\{DUU\}$	$q \times p \times p = p^2q$	$\{DDD\}$	$q \times q \times q = q^3$

If we let E_3 be the event that the tack lands point up all 3 times, let E_2 be the event that it lands point up 2 times out of 3, let E_1 be the event that it lands point up 1 time out of 3, and let E_0 be the event that it lands point down all 3 times, then $P(E_3) = p^3$, $P(E_2) = 3p^2q$, $P(E_1) = 3pq^2$, and $P(E_0) = q^3$.

If the tack is tossed n times, the sample space for the compound experiment is $T_1 \times T_2 \times \ldots \times T_n$, where $T_i = T$, for $i = 1, 2, \ldots, n$. If the tosses are independent, the probability of each simple event in $T_1 \times T_2 \times \ldots \times T_n$ is computed by means of the multiplication rule for independent experiments, as illustrated for the case $n = 3$ in the table above. If the simple event includes r *ups* and $n - r$ *downs*, its probability is $p^r q^{n-r}$. If E_r is the event that the tack lands point up r times out of n, then this can happen in $\binom{n}{r}$ distinct ways, each of which has probability $p^r q^{n-r}$. Then $P(E_r) = \binom{n}{r} p^r q^{n-r}$.

The case of n repeated independent tosses of a tack is examined in greater detail in Chapter IX, which is devoted entirely to this important compound experiment.

Exercises for Chapter V

1. Two fair dice are rolled. What is the probability that at least one of the dice turns up a 3?

2. Using the data for the class of 30 children described on page 108, if a child in the class is chosen at random, what is the probability that the child is a boy or is on the honor roll?

3. If a card is drawn at random from a bridge deck, what is the probability that it is an ace or a spade?

4. Five fair coins are tossed. What is the probability that the number of heads exceeds the number of tails?

5. At a Christmas party for a kindergarten class of 15 children, all of whom are from different families, each child is accompanied by his mother and father. There is a separate door prize for mothers, fathers, and children, awarded in each group by selecting a person at random. What is the probability that a particular family wins at least one prize?

6. Using the data and definitions given for the set of 10 householders listed in the table on page 105, find $P(E \mid G)$, the conditional probability that a householder is a Republican, given that his income is over \$7,000 per year.

7. Using the data and definitions given on page 108 for a class of 30 children, compare $P(H \mid B)$ with $P(B \mid H)$. Are they the same?

8. Johnny washes the supper dishes twice a week, and his older brother Frank does them 5 times a week. Johnny's two days are chosen at random each week. The probability that Johnny will break one or more dishes during a washing is .1, and the probability that Frank will is .02. One evening, as the dishes were being done, Dad heard a dish crash. He said to Mom, "Apparently this is Johnny's dish day." What is the probability that he was right?

9. In a factory there are four machines, I, II, III, and IV, that make nails. Their share of the total output is 15%, 20%, 30%, and 35% respectively. Defective nails produced by each machine are 5%, 4%, 3% and 2% of its own output, respectively. A nail chosen at random from the total output of the factory is found to be defective. What are the probabilities that it was made by machine I, II, III, IV?

10. The incidence of myxoedema (underactive thyroid gland) among people admitted to hospitals is about 1 in 1500.

Doctors often use the "protein-bound iodine test" to determine whether or not a person has myxoedema. When the test is used on people who have myxoedema, it shows the presence of the disease in 90% of those tested. In the remaining 10% the test yields a false negative result. When the test is given to people who do not have myxoedema, it shows the absence of the disease in 99% of those tested. In the remaining 1% the test yields a false positive result. If the test is used on a hospital patient chosen at random, and the result is positive (indicating that the patient has myxoedema) what is the probability that the patient really has myxoedema?

11. If E and F are independent events, prove that E and F' are independent. (Hint: $E \cap F'$ and $E \cap F$ are mutually exclusive events whose union is E.)

12. Define E and F as we did on page 115, for families with a given number of children. For families with 4 children, are E and F independent events?

13. An urn contains 6 white balls and 12 black balls. If a ball is drawn from it at random, we may use $S = \{w, b\}$ as sample space, with appropriate assignment of probabilities. Another urn contains 4 red balls, 6 yellow balls, and 10 green balls. If a ball is drawn at random from this urn, we may use $T = \{r, y, g\}$ as sample space with appropriate assignment of probabilities. If a ball is drawn at random, and independently, from each urn, the outcome is an element of $S \times T$. What is the probability of each simple event in S? in T? in $S \times T$? Summarize your answer in the form of a tree diagram.

CHAPTER VI

The Average, and Deviations from It

Random Variables

IN SOME probability experiments we assign a definite real number, according to some rule, to each element of the sample space for the experiment. Such an assignment of real numbers to elements of a sample space is called a *random variable*. For a finite sample space a random variable can be represented by a table which lists each element of the sample space and shows what number is assigned to it. To make this concept clear, we give some examples.

Number of Heads. Perform the experiment of tossing four fair coins. Assign to each outcome the number of heads that turn up. This random variable is expressed in the following table:

Outcome	HHHH	HHHT	HHTH	HTHH	THHH	HHTT	HTHT	HTTH
No. of Heads	4	3	3	3	3	2	2	2
Outcome	THHT	THTH	TTHH	HTTT	THTT	TTHT	TTTH	TTTT
No. of Heads	2	2	2	1	1	1	1	0

When we talk about a random variable we find it convenient to designate it by a capital letter. If we let X stand for the random variable expressed in the table above, we make use of the designation in this way: To say that the number assigned to the outcome *HHHT* is 3, we write $X(HHHT) = 3$. Read this as "The value of X at *HHHT* equals 3," or, more briefly, "X at *HHHT* equals 3." Thus, the statement that $X(THTT) = 1$ expresses the fact that the random variable X assigns the number 1 to the outcome *THTT*.

Two-Dice Sum. Perform the experiment of rolling two fair dice. Assign to each outcome the sum of the numbers that turn up. We show only part of the table for this random variable:

Outcome	(1, 1)	(1, 2)	(1, 3)	(1, 4)	(1, 5)	(1, 6)	(2, 1)	. . .
Sum	2	3	4	5	6	7	3	. . .

If we let Y stand for this random variable, some additional values of Y are given in these statements: $Y((2, 4)) = 6,$ $Y((5, 3)) = 8$.

Number On a Die. Perform the experiment of rolling one fair die. Assign to each outcome the number that turns up. The table for this random variable is:

Outcome	1	2	3	4	5	6
Number	1	2	3	4	5	6

The entries on both lines of this table are the same because we have followed our usual custom of designating each outcome by means of the number that turns up when that outcome occurs. If we call this random variable Z, we may write $Z(k) = k$, for $k = 1, 2, 3, 4, 5, 6$.

Population Data. Any group of people may be considered a sample space, with each person an element of the sample space. A random variable is defined if we assign to each person the number of inches in his height, or the number of pounds in his weight, or the number of dollars in his annual income, etc.

Probability Functions

Let S be the sample space of 16 possible outcomes for the experiment of tossing four fair coins, and examine the table for the random variable X which specifies the number of heads at each outcome. This table can be read in two directions. If we read it from the top down, then, for any outcome that we pick, the table assigns exactly one value of X. For example, if we pick the outcome $HHTT$, the table assigns the value $X(HHTT) = 2$. However, if we read it from the bottom up, then, for any value of X that appears in the table, the table assigns one or more outcomes. For example, if we pick the value $X = 2$, the table assigns the outcomes $HHTT$, $HTHT$, $HTTH$, $THHT$, $THTH$, and $TTHH$. That is, the table, when read backwards, assigns to each value of X that appears in the table a *set* of outcomes in S, or an event in S. Moreover, it even makes an assignment to values of X that do not appear in the table. For example, the numbers -1 and 5 do not appear in the table. Hence the set of elements of S assigned to these numbers is empty. Consequently, while no element of S is assigned to these numbers, there is an event in S that is assigned to them, namely $\emptyset$. This assignment of events to values of X is summarized in the first two columns of the table at the top of page 127. There are many more values of X, not listed in the table, to which the empty set is assigned. These include all numbers not found on the second line of the table for the random variable.

Value of X	Event in S	Probability of the Event
-1	$\emptyset$	0
0	$\{TTTT\}$	$\frac{1}{16}$
1	$\{HTTT, THTT, TTHT, TTTH\}$	$\frac{4}{16}$
2	$\{HHTT, HTHT, HTTH, THHT, THTH, TTHH\}$	$\frac{6}{16}$
3	$\{HHHT, HHTH, HTHH, THHH\}$	$\frac{4}{16}$
4	$\{HHHH\}$	$\frac{1}{16}$
5	$\emptyset$	0

The third column of the table shows the probability of each event listed in the second column. Since the table assigns an event to each value of X, and since each such event has a definite probability, the table automatically assigns a probability number to each value of X, namely the probability of the event that X has that value. This assignment may be shown in a separate table in which only the first and third columns of the table above are used. We print it below in a horizontal rather than a vertical arrangement in order to save space. We also omit those values of X that are assigned the probability number 0.

Value of X	0	1	2	3	4
Probability of the event that X has the value shown	$\frac{1}{16}$	$\frac{4}{16}$	$\frac{6}{16}$	$\frac{4}{16}$	$\frac{1}{16}$

The assignments shown in this new table constitute what is called a *probability function*. If we designate by f the probability function shown in the table above, then for each real number x, $f(x)$ represents the probability of the event that $X = x$. That is, $f(x) = P$(the event that $X = x$). (P(the event that $X = x$) will sometimes be written in abbreviated form: $P(X = x)$). For example, in the table above, $f(0) = \frac{1}{16}$, $f(1) = \frac{4}{16}$, etc. Since the events shown in the table are mutually exclusive in pairs, and their union is S, the sum of the probabilities shown in the table is equal to 1. That is, $f(0) + f(1) + f(2) + f(3) + f(4) = 1$.

In the same way, a probability function is automatically defined for every random variable X over a sample space S for whose events probabilities have been defined. The probability function assigns to each real number x the probability of the event that the variable X has the value x. If f is the probability function defined by $f(x) = P$(the event that $X = x$), let $x_1, x_2, \ldots, x_k$ be the set of all possible values of X, that is, those for which $f(x) \neq 0$. Then

$$(1) \qquad f(x_1) + f(x_2) + \ldots + f(x_k) = 1.$$

A probability function can be shown graphically by representing all real numbers as points on a horizontal line, and erecting over each point x a vertical bar whose length represents $f(x)$. The graph below shows the probability function for the random variable $X =$ the number of heads when four fair coins are tossed.

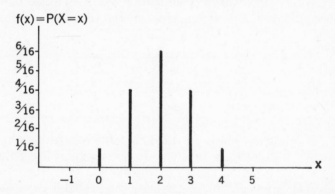

In the preceding section of this chapter we defined the random variable $Y =$ the sum turned up when two fair dice are rolled, and the random variable $Z =$ the number turned up when a single fair die is rolled. The table and graph for the probability function determined by each of these random variables is on page 129.

Value of Y	2	3	4	5	6	7
Probability of the event that Y has the value shown	$\frac{1}{36}$	$\frac{2}{36}$	$\frac{3}{36}$	$\frac{4}{36}$	$\frac{5}{36}$	$\frac{6}{36}$

Value of Y	8	9	10	11	12	
Probability of the event that Y has the value shown	$\frac{5}{36}$	$\frac{4}{36}$	$\frac{3}{36}$	$\frac{2}{36}$	$\frac{1}{36}$	

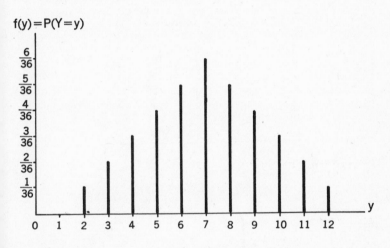

Value of Z	1	2	3	4	5	6
Probability of the event that Z has the value shown	$\frac{1}{6}$	$\frac{1}{6}$	$\frac{1}{6}$	$\frac{1}{6}$	$\frac{1}{6}$	$\frac{1}{6}$

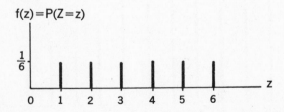

As another example of a probability function, we shall display one that is derived from some population data. As part of a study to determine the influence of heredity on height, heights measured to the nearest inch were tabulated for 114 men whose fathers were 6 ft. 1 in. tall. Four of the men were 67 inches tall. So, if a man were

Heights of 114 Men Whose Fathers Were 6 ft. 1 in. Tall.

w = Height (Nearest Inch)	Probability $f(w) = P(W = w)$	w = Height (Nearest Inch)	Probability $f(w) = P(W = w)$
67	.04	74	.11
68	.08	75	.06
69	.08	76	.04
70	.12	77	.05
71	.17	78	.03
72	.10	79	.01
73	.11		
		Total	1.00

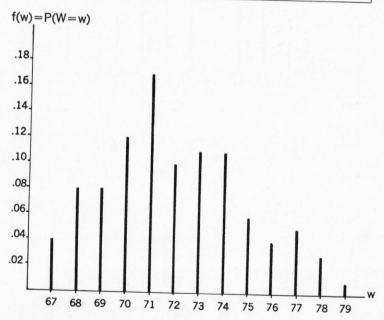

chosen at random from among the 114 men, the probability that his height would be 67 inches is $\frac{4}{114}$, or approximately .04. The probability of each of the heights that occurred among the 114 men was calculated in the same way. The heights of the men determine a random variable W. The resulting probability function $f(w)$ determined by the heights of the men is shown in the table and graph on page 130.

New Variables From Old

If X is a random variable defined over a sample space S, expressions like $2X$, $X + 3$, $2X + 3$, and X^2 are examples of what mathematicians call *functions* of the variable. Each such expression gives directions for calculating a new number to be associated with each value of X. For example, the expression $2X$ says, "Whatever the value of X is, double it." Thus, when $X = 5$, $2X = 10$. The expression $X + 3$ says, "Whatever the value of X is, add 3 to it." So, when $X = 5$, $X + 3 = 8$. The expression $2X + 3$ says, "Whatever the value of X is, double it and then add 3." So, when $X = 5$, $2X + 3 = 13$. The expression X^2 says, "Whatever the value of X is, multiply it by itself. So, when $X = 5$, $X^2 = 25$.

The random variable X assigns a definite number to each element of S. A function of X associates a new number with this one, and so, indirectly assigns the new number to the corresponding element of S. In this way, a function of X is itself a random variable. For example, for $X =$ the number of heads turned up when four fair coins are tossed, the table below shows values of X, $2X$, $X + 3$, $2X + 3$, and X^2 for each possible outcome of the experiment. The first and third column together define the random variable $2X$, the first and fourth column together define the random variable $X + 3$, and so on. Each of these new random variables determines a probability function in the same way that the random variable X does.

Outcome	x	$2x$	$x + 3$	$2x + 3$	x^2
HHHH	4	8	7	11	16
HHHT	3	6	6	9	9
HHTH	3	6	6	9	9
HTHH	3	6	6	9	9
THHH	3	6	6	9	9
HHTT	2	4	5	7	4
HTHT	2	4	5	7	4
HTTH	2	4	5	7	4
THHT	2	4	5	7	4
THTH	2	4	5	7	4
TTHH	2	4	5	7	4
HTTT	1	2	4	5	1
THTT	1	2	4	5	1
TTHT	1	2	4	5	1
TTTH	1	2	4	5	1
TTTT	0	0	3	3	0

Thumb-Nail Sketch of a Probability Function

Every person is a unique combination of physical, mental and personality traits. The number of traits in a person's makeup is extremely numerous, if not actually infinite. When an author of a novel introduces one of his characters for the first time, he does not try to enumerate all these traits. Instead, he often resorts to the device of giving a thumb-nail sketch of the character. In this sketch he describes a *few* significant traits of the character that help you to visualize him quickly.

We face a similar problem in the study of probability functions. Every probability function is a unique combination of traits that can be presented fully by displaying the table or the graph of the function. However, for many purposes we do not need all the known details about the function. It is often good enough to have only a thumbnail sketch of the function, made up of just a few significant traits that help us see approximately what the graph looks like. The chief purpose of the rest of this chapter is to define and use two such traits that can serve to characterize a probability function. Each of these traits is a number that is significantly related to the appearance of the graph of the function. The first of these numbers is a sort of middle value of the random variable around which the bars of the graph tend to cluster. The second of these numbers measures the extent to which the possible values of the random variable are dispersed about this middle value.

The Expectation or Average

The middle value that we shall use is the one commonly known as the *average* or *mean value* of the random variable. In probability theory it is also known as the *expectation* of the variable. If X is a random variable whose possible values are $x_1, x_2, \ldots, x_k$, and the event that each occurs has probability $f(x_1), f(x_2), \ldots, f(x_k)$ respectively, then we denote the expectation of X by $E(X)$, and define it as follows:

$$(2) \qquad E(X) = x_1 f(x_1) + x_2 f(x_2) + \ldots + x_k f(x_k).$$

This equation tells us that, *to compute the expectation of a random variable, multiply each possible value of the variable by the probability of the event that it occurs, and then add the products*. The computation is shown below for each of the following random variables already introduced in this chapter: X = number of heads when four fair coins are tossed, Y = the sum that turns up when two fair dice are rolled, Z = the number that turns up when one fair die is rolled, and W = the height of a man in the group of 114 men whose fathers are 6 ft. 1 in. tall.

x	$f(x) = P(X = x)$	$xf(x)$
0	$\frac{1}{16}$	0
1	$\frac{4}{16}$	$\frac{4}{16}$
2	$\frac{6}{16}$	$\frac{12}{16}$
3	$\frac{4}{16}$	$\frac{12}{16}$
4	$\frac{1}{16}$	$\frac{4}{16}$
$E(X) = \frac{32}{16} = 2.$		$\frac{32}{16}$

z	$f(z) = P(Z = z)$	$zf(z)$
1	$\frac{1}{6}$	$\frac{1}{6}$
2	$\frac{1}{6}$	$\frac{2}{6}$
3	$\frac{1}{6}$	$\frac{3}{6}$
4	$\frac{1}{6}$	$\frac{4}{6}$
5	$\frac{1}{6}$	$\frac{5}{6}$
6	$\frac{1}{6}$	$\frac{6}{6}$
$E(Z) = \frac{21}{6} = 3.5$		$\frac{21}{6}$

y	$f(y) = P(Y = y)$	$yf(y)$
2	$\frac{1}{36}$	$\frac{2}{36}$
3	$\frac{2}{36}$	$\frac{6}{36}$
4	$\frac{3}{36}$	$\frac{12}{36}$
5	$\frac{4}{36}$	$\frac{20}{36}$
6	$\frac{5}{36}$	$\frac{30}{36}$
7	$\frac{6}{36}$	$\frac{42}{36}$
8	$\frac{5}{36}$	$\frac{40}{36}$
9	$\frac{4}{36}$	$\frac{36}{36}$
10	$\frac{3}{36}$	$\frac{30}{36}$
11	$\frac{2}{36}$	$\frac{22}{36}$
12	$\frac{1}{36}$	$\frac{12}{36}$
$E(Y) = \frac{252}{36} = 7.$		$\frac{252}{36}$

w	$f(w) = P(W = w)$	$wf(w)$
67	.04	2.68
68	.08	5.44
69	.08	5.52
70	.12	8.40
71	.17	12.07
72	.10	7.20
73	.11	8.03
74	.11	8.14
75	.06	4.50
76	.04	3.04
77	.05	3.85
78	.03	2.34
79	.01	.79
$E(W) = 72.$		72.00

Chuck-a-luck. The game chuck-a-luck, often played at carnivals, is played according to the following rules. The player pays a fee to play the game. Then he picks a number from 1 to 6. He rolls three dice. If his number comes up on all three dice, he is paid four times his fee. If the number comes up on exactly two of the dice, he is paid three times his fee. If the number comes up on exactly one of the dice, he is paid double his fee. If the number comes up on none of the dice, he is paid nothing. If the fee is $1, and the outcomes on the three dice are assumed to be three independent events, what is the expected gain of the player? The gain of the player is a random variable equal to the number of dollars in his winnings minus his fee. Let's call this random variable X, and its probability function f. If we use Y, (for "yes"), to indicate the event that the player's number has turned up on a die, then $P(Y)$ on a single die is $\frac{1}{6}$, and $P(Y')$ on a single die is $\frac{5}{6}$. Since the outcomes on the separate dice are assumed to be independent, the probability of any particular outcome of tossing all three dice may be calculated by the multiplication rule. These probabilities are shown in the table below:

Possible Outcome	Probability
$Y\ Y\ Y$	$\frac{1}{6} \times \frac{1}{6} \times \frac{1}{6} = \frac{1}{216}$
$Y\ Y\ Y'$	$\frac{1}{6} \times \frac{1}{6} \times \frac{5}{6} = \frac{5}{216}$
$Y\ Y'\ Y$	$\frac{1}{6} \times \frac{5}{6} \times \frac{1}{6} = \frac{5}{216}$
$Y'\ Y\ Y$	$\frac{5}{6} \times \frac{1}{6} \times \frac{1}{6} = \frac{5}{216}$
$Y\ Y'\ Y'$	$\frac{1}{6} \times \frac{5}{6} \times \frac{5}{6} = \frac{25}{216}$
$Y'\ Y\ Y'$	$\frac{5}{6} \times \frac{1}{6} \times \frac{5}{6} = \frac{25}{216}$
$Y'\ Y'\ Y$	$\frac{5}{6} \times \frac{5}{6} \times \frac{1}{6} = \frac{25}{215}$
$Y'\ Y'\ Y'$	$\frac{5}{6} \times \frac{5}{6} \times \frac{5}{6} = \frac{125}{216}$

The next table shows the possible values x of the random variable X, the event that $X = x$, the corresponding probability $f(x) = P(X = x)$, and the product $xf(x)$.

Gain x (in \$)	The event $X = x$	$f(x)$	$xf(x)$
3	$\{Y\ Y\ Y\}$	$\frac{1}{216}$	$\frac{3}{216}$
2	$\{Y\ Y\ Y',\ Y\ Y'\ Y,\ Y'\ Y\ Y\}$	$\frac{15}{216}$	$\frac{30}{216}$
1	$\{Y\ Y'\ Y',\ Y'\ Y\ Y',\ Y'\ Y'\ Y\}$	$\frac{75}{216}$	$\frac{75}{216}$
−1	$\{Y'\ Y'\ Y'\}$	$\frac{125}{216}$	$-\frac{125}{216}$

$$E(X) = \frac{3}{216} + \frac{30}{216} + \frac{75}{216} - \frac{125}{216} = -\frac{17}{216} = -.08.$$

The minus sign indicates that the expectation is a loss rather than a gain. The expected loss is about 8¢. Intuitively we feel that this means that although a player may gain money in some games and lose money in others, if he plays many games he will probably average a loss of 8¢ per game in the long run. In the next chapter we shall see that there is a basic truth underlying this intuitive notion. *Blood Test.* Part of the pre-induction physical examination for the armed forces is a blood test for syphilis. A substantial amount of time, effort and money is saved by pooling blood samples of several people at a time and testing the pooled sample, rather than testing each person's blood separately. If the test reaction of the pooled sample is negative, then it is known to be negative for each person whose blood is in the sample, so one test has taken the place of many. If the test reaction of the pooled sample is positive, then it is necessary to take fresh blood samples from the people whose blood is in it, and test these samples separately to find out whose blood has the positive reaction. In this case one test has been wasted. But the number of negative reactions far overshadows the number of positive reactions, so the net result when many people are tested is a saving in the number of tests. If the incidence of syphilis is known, it is possible to calculate how many blood samples should be pooled in order to effect the greatest possible saving.

We shall make this calculation using the data of the Selective Service Administration for the years 1940 and 1941. The incidence of syphilis among men aged 21 to 35 was found to be 45.3 per thousand. Then, for individual blood tests made at random, the probability of a positive reaction is about 5%, and the probability of a negative reaction is about 95%. Let us assume that tests of different individuals are independent trials. Let k be the number of individual samples that are combined in the pooled sample, where k is an integer that is greater than 1. There are two possible events when the pooled sample is tested: the reaction will be negative or positive. The reaction is negative if and only if each of the k blood samples that are mixed has a negative reaction. By the multiplication rule for independent trials, the probability that this will happen is $(.95)^k$. Consequently, the probability of a positive reaction by the pooled sample is $1 - (.95)^k$. The number of blood tests that have to be made for each group of k people tested is a random variable which we shall designate by X. When the reaction of the pooled sample is negative, $X = 1$. When the reaction is positive, $X = k + 1$, since k fresh samples are then taken to be tested separately.

The expected number of tests that have to be made per k people is $E(X)$. Had individual tests been made in the first place, the number of tests per k people would have been k. So the expected saving is $k - E(X)$ tests per k people. Then the expected fraction saved is $(k - E(X))/k$. The procedure for calculating this fraction is shown below:

x = no. of tests	Event	$f(x) = P(X = x)$	$xf(x)$
1	negative	$(.95)^k$	$(.95)^k$
$k + 1$	positive	$1 - (.95)^k$	$(k + 1)(1 - (.95)^k)$

$E(X) = (.95)^k + (k + 1)(1 - (.95)^k) = k + 1 - k(.95)^k$.
Expected saving $= k - E(X) = k(.95)^k - 1 = N - 1$, where N designates $k(.95)^k$. The expected fraction saved is $(N - 1)/k$. We show the calculation of this fraction for $k = 4$, 5, and 6.

$\log 4 = .6021$	$\log 5 = .6990$	$\log 6 = .7782$
$4 \log .95 = .9108 - 1$	$5 \log .95 = .8885 - 1$	$6 \log .95 = .8662 - 1$
$\log N = 1.5129 - 1$	$\log N = 1.5875 - 1$	$\log N = 1.6444 - 1$
$N = 3.26$,	$N = 3.87$,	$N = 4.41$,
$N - 1 = 2.26$.	$N - 1 = 2.87$.	$N - 1 = 3.41$.
Fraction saved $=$	Fraction saved $=$	Fraction saved $=$
$\dfrac{N - 1}{k} = \dfrac{2.26}{4}$	$\dfrac{N - 1}{k} = \dfrac{2.87}{5}$	$\dfrac{N - 1}{k} = \dfrac{3.41}{6}$
$= 56.5\%$	$= 57.4\%$	$= 56.8\%$

Calculation of the expected fraction saved for successive values of k shows that the fraction increases as k increases from 2 to 5. Then it declines for higher values of k. Therefore the most economical way of testing the blood samples is to mix 5 samples at a time.

The Petersburg Paradox. Suppose a gambler plays a game governed by the following rules: 1) He tosses a fair coin repeatedly until it turns up heads for the first time, but he makes no more than 5 tosses. 2) If the first head occurs on the k'th toss, where k is not larger than 5, then he receives 2^k dollars. If no head occurs in the 5 tosses, he receives nothing. What is his expected gain?

The possible outcomes in this game are H, TH, TTH, $TTTH$, $TTTTH$, $TTTTT$. The probability of heads in a single toss is $\frac{1}{2}$. Assuming that repeated tosses are independent trials, the probability of each of these outcomes may be calculated by the multiplication rule for independent trials. The number of dollars won in a game is a random variable which we shall call X. The expected gain is $E(X)$. The data needed for calculating $E(X)$ are recorded in the following table:

x	The event $X = x$	$f(x) = P(X = x)$	$xf(x)$
2	$\{H\}$	$\frac{1}{2}$	1
2^2	$\{TH\}$	$(\frac{1}{2})^2$	1
2^3	$\{TTH\}$	$(\frac{1}{2})^3$	1
2^4	$\{TTTH\}$	$(\frac{1}{2})^4$	1
2^5	$\{TTTTH\}$	$(\frac{1}{2})^5$	1
0	$\{TTTTT\}$	$(\frac{1}{2})^5$	0

Adding up the numbers in the last column, we find that $E(X) = 5$.

Now suppose that the gambler must pay an entrance fee for the privilege of playing this game. In the ancient lore of gambling, an entrance fee is considered "fair" if it is equal to the expected gain. In this case, then, a fair entrance fee is $5.

The game can be generalized by letting the maximum number of tosses allowed be any positive integer n. Then, by similar reasoning we find that the expected gain is n dollars, and, hence, a fair entrance fee is n dollars.

In the Petersburg game, famous in the literature of probability theory since the eighteenth century, the game is played in the same way, except that there is no upper limit on the number of tosses allowed. What is a fair entrance fee for the Petersburg game? This is like asking, "What is the limit of the expected gain, n dollars, as n increases without limit?" The answer, of course, is that there is no such limit. It used to be the custom to say that the limit is *infinite*, and hence a fair entrance fee is infinite.

It is possible to assign to the Petersburg game a fair entrance fee that is finite provided that we modify the concept of a fair entrance fee in several ways: 1) We consider not just one game, but an infinite sequence of games, played one after the other. 2) We allow the entrance fee to vary from game to game, instead of requiring a fixed entrance fee for each game. 3) We consider the game fair if, for a very large number of games, the ratio of the total winnings to the total of the entrance fees paid is probably close to 1. It is shown in advanced books on probability theory that under these conditions the fee is fair if the total entrance fee for the first n games is $(n \log n)/\log 2$.

Expectation of a Function of a Random Variable

Let X be a random variable over a sample space, and let Y be a real-valued function of X. We saw on page 131 that Y is also a random variable over the same sample space. We consider here the problem of calculating the expectation of Y. To show concretely what the problem is, and how we solve it we shall examine a special case. The solution we shall develop, however, is perfectly general and may be extended to the general case.

Let X be a random variable whose possible values are -2, -1, 0, 1, 2. Let the associated probability function be f. That is, $f(x) = P(X = x)$. Let $Y = X^2$. Denote by E_x the event that $X = x$. Then $f(x) = P(E_x)$. The information we shall need to calculate $E(Y)$ will be drawn from the following table:

x	E_x	$f(x) = P(E_x)$	$y = x^2$
-2	E_{-2}	$f(-2)$	4
-1	E_{-1}	$f(-1)$	1
0	E_0	$f(0)$	0
1	E_1	$f(1)$	1
2	E_2	$f(2)$	4

The definition of expectation tells us that *to calculate $E(Y)$ we must multiply each possible value of Y by the probability of the event that that value of Y occurs, and then we must add all these products.* To help us follow these directions easily we prepare a new table in which we tabulate each possible value y, the event that $Y = y$, the probability $P(Y = y)$, and the product $yP(Y = y)$. The table will necessarily take into account that $Y = 4$ when $X = -2$ or 2. Therefore the event that $Y = 4$ is the union of the events E_{-2} and E_2. Since these two events are mutually exclusive, $P(Y = 4) = f(-2) + f(2)$. Similarly, $P(Y = 1) = f(-1) + f(1)$. Here is the new table:

y	The event that $Y = y$	$P(Y = y)$	$yP(Y = y)$
0	E_0	$f(0)$	$0(f(0))$
1	$E_{-1} \cup E_1$	$f(-1) + f(1)$	$1(f(-1) + f(1))$
4	$E_2 \cup E_2$	$f(-2) + f(2)$	$4(f(-2) + f(2))$

To find $E(Y)$, we add the terms in the last column of this table. So $E(Y) = 0f(0) + 1(f(-1) + f(1)) + 4(f(-2) +$

$f(2)$). We shall now try to express this sum *in terms of the possible values of X*. First we carry through the indicated multiplications by 1 and 4 in the expression for $E(Y)$. We get $E(Y) = 0f(0) + 1f(-1) + 1f(1) + 4f(-2) + 4f(2)$. We now rewrite the numbers 1 and 4 in a way which shows how we calculated them in the first place from values of X. In the second term on the right hand side of the equation, replace 1 by $(-1)^2$. In the third term, replace 1 by $(1)^2$. In the fourth term, replace 4 by $(-2)^2$. In the fifth term, replace 4 by $(2)^2$. Then we have

$$E(Y) = 0f(0) + (-1)^2 f(-1) + (1)^2 f(1) \\ + (-2)^2 f(-2) + (2)^2 f(2).$$

An examination of this equation gives us the new rule for calculating $E(Y)$: *For each possible value x of X, find the corresponding value of Y and multiply it by $f(x)$. Then add all these products.* Similar reasoning leads to the same rule, even if Y is *any* real-valued function of X, and X is *any* random variable. We shall now use the rule to show how, in some important special cases, we can express $E(Y)$ in terms of $E(X)$.

Adding a Fixed Number to X. Let X be a random variable with expectation $E(X)$. If we add a fixed number b to each value of X, what effect does it have on the expectation? In other words, what is $E(Y)$ if $Y = X + b$? We shall answer this question by an intuitive argument first, and then we shall confirm the answer by means of a computation.

Consider the probability function f associated with the random variable X. We may visualize f by means of its graph, in which there is a vertical bar with length $f(x)$ erected at each possible value x of X. $E(X)$, the average value of X, is a kind of middle value of x around which these bars cluster. If we add b to each value of X, this is like moving the whole graph b units, to the right if b is positive, and to the left if b is negative. Then the middle value is also moved the same distance. Consequently, $E(X + b) = E(X) + b$.

To confirm this result, let the possible values of X be $x_1, x_2, \ldots, x_k$. By definition, $E(X) = x_1f(x_1) + x_2f(x_2) + \ldots + x_kf(x_k)$. According to the rule we have just derived for calculating $E(Y)$,

$$E(X + b) = (x_1 + b)f(x_1) + (x_2 + b)f(x_2) \\ + \ldots (x_k + b)f(x_k).$$

Carrying through the indicated multiplications and rearranging the order of the terms, we get

$$E(X + b) = x_1f(x_1) + x_2f(x_2) + \ldots + x_kf(x_k) \\ + bf(x_1) + bf(x_2) + \ldots + bf(x_k).$$

The sum $x_1f(x_1) + x_2f(x_2) + \ldots + x_kf(x_k)$ is equal to $E(X)$. The sum $bf(x_1) + bf(x_2) + \ldots + bf(x_k) = b(f(x_1) + f(x_2) + \ldots + f(x_k)) = b \times 1 = b$, since $f(x_1) + f(x_2) + \ldots + f(x_k) = 1$. Making these substitutions, we find that

$$(3) \qquad E(X + b) = E(X) + b.$$

Multiplying X by a Fixed Number. If we multiply each value of X by a fixed number a, what effect does it have on the expectation? In other words, what is $E(Y)$ if $Y = aX$? We shall answer this question too by an intuitive argument first, and then we shall confirm the answer by means of a computation.

For the intuitive argument, we consider again the graph of the probability function associated with the random variable X. Multiplying each value of X by a is like a change in scale for drawing the horizontal distances in the graph. We can visualize this change as a uniform horizontal stretching or contraction of the sheet on which the graph is drawn. This change in scale affects all horizontal measurements in the same way. Consequently the average value of X, which is a sort of middle position in the graph, will also be multiplied by a. Therefore

(4) $$E(ax) = aE(X).$$

To confirm this result, let the possible values of X be $x_1, x_2, \ldots, x_k$. According to the rule for calculating $E(Y)$,

$$E(aX) = (ax_1)f(x_1) + (ax_2)f(x_2) + \ldots + (ax_k)f(x_k)$$
$$= a(x_1f(x_1) + x_2f(x_2) + \ldots + x_kf(x_k)) = aE(X).$$

The Expectation of $aX + b$. To calculate $E(aX + b)$, we consider the three random variables X, Y, and Z, where $Y = aX$, and $Z = Y + b$. $E(aX + b) = E(Y + b) = E(Y) + b$, according to the rule we just discovered for the case where a fixed number is added to each value of a random variable. But $E(Y) = E(aX) = aE(X)$, according to the rule for the case where each value of a random variable is multiplied by a fixed number. Then $E(aX + b) = aE(X) + b$.

To show how this rule is used, we apply it to some specific examples. 1) Let X be the number of heads that turn up when four fair coins are tossed. Find $E(3X + 5)$. Our formula says that $E(3X + 5) = 3E(X) + 5$. We found on page 134 that $E(X) = 2$. Therefore $E(3X + 5) = 3 \times 2 + 5 = 11$. 2) Let $Y =$ the sum of the numbers that turn up when two fair dice are rolled. Find $E(\frac{1}{2}Y - 3)$. Our formula says that $E(\frac{1}{2}Y - 3) = \frac{1}{2}E(Y) - 3$. We found on page 134 that $E(Y) = 7$. Therefore $E(\frac{1}{2}Y - 3) = \frac{1}{2} \times 7 - 3 = .5$. 3) Let X be any random variable, and denote by the Greek letter μ, (mu), the value of $E(X)$. Find $E(X - \mu)$. Our formula tells us that $E(X - \mu) = E(X) - \mu = \mu - \mu = 0$. *If the mean value is subtracted from each value of a random variable, a new random variable is obtained whose mean value is zero.*

Variance and Standard Deviation

We now turn to the problem of finding a measure of the extent to which the possible values of a random variable are dispersed about its expected value. Let X be the random variable, and let $E(X) = \mu$. First consider each possible value x of X by itself. To find out how much x deviates from μ, simply take their difference $x - \mu$. In this way we get a new random variable $X - \mu$ which we shall call the *deviation of* X. However, this is not the measure of dispersion that we are looking for, because it gives us a set of numbers, one for each possible value of X, rather than a single number that characterizes the behavior of all the possible values of X. We are tempted to get such a single number by finding the average value of the deviation. However, the average of the deviation of X is $E(X - \mu)$, and we have just seen that this is equal to 0. The average of the deviation of X collapses to 0 because there are values of X on both sides of μ. For those values of X that are to the right of μ, the deviation $X - \mu$ is positive. For those values of X that are to the left of μ, the deviation $X - \mu$ is negative. Precisely because μ is the average value of X, the negative and positive values of the deviation cancel each other out when we average them. So $E(X - \mu)$ is useless as a collective measure of the dispersion of the values of X.

However, knowing why $E(X - \mu)$ is useless suggests how we might define a measure that will be useful. If we assign to each value of X a *non-negative* number related to its deviation, and then average these numbers, the average will not collapse to 0 unless all the numbers assigned were equal to 0 in the first place. There are many ways in which this might be done. The method that turns out to be most useful is to square the deviation. This defines a new random variable, $(X - \mu)^2$. The average, $E((X - \mu)^2)$, of this new random variable is called the variance of X, and is denoted by Var (X). This is not yet the measure that we want, however. The unit of measure for Var (X) is the square of the unit of measure of X, because in the definition of Var (X) we begin by squaring $X - \mu$. To restore the original unit of measure we undo the effect of squaring by taking the square root. This leads to the following definition: the *standard deviation* of $X =$ $\sqrt{\text{Var}(X)} = \sqrt{E((X-\mu)^2)}$. The standard deviation is the measure of dispersion that we were looking for. We shall usually denote it by the Greek letter σ, (sigma).

The definition of the standard deviation of X gives us directions for computing it. The directions require this sequence of steps: First compute $\mu = E(X)$. Then, for each value of X, compute $X - \mu$. Then square $(X - \mu)$ to get $(X - \mu)^2$. Then compute $\text{Var}(X) = E((X-\mu)^2)$. Then take the square root of $\text{Var}(X)$. As an example, we compute the standard deviation of the random variable W defined on page 130. The first three columns of the table below merely repeat the table that appears on page 134.

w	$f(w) = P(W = w)$	$wf(w)$	$w - \mu$	$(w - \mu)^2$	$(w - \mu)^2 f(w)$
67	.04	2.68	−5	25	1.00
68	.08	5.44	−4	16	1.28
69	.08	5.52	−3	9	.72
70	.12	8.40	−2	4	.48
71	.17	12.07	−1	1	.17
72	.10	7.20	0	0	0.00
73	.11	8.03	1	1	.11
74	.11	8.14	2	4	.44
75	.06	4.50	3	9	.54
76	.04	3.04	4	16	.64
77	.05	3.85	5	25	1.25
78	.03	2.34	6	36	1.08
79	.01	.79	7	49	.49

$$E(W) = \mu = 72.00 \qquad \text{Var}(W) = 8.20$$

$$\sigma = \sqrt{\text{Var}(W)} = \sqrt{8.20} = 2.9.$$

There is another way of computing the standard deviation of a random variable X that is based on a formula that expresses $\text{Var}(X)$ in terms of $E(X^2)$ and $E(X)$. Since we shall need this formula for other purposes as well, we derive it now. In order to make it easy to follow all the details of the derivation, we shall assume that X has only

146 *Probability and Statistics for Everyman*

three possible values, x_1, x_2, and x_3. However, the same procedure may be followed if X has any finite number of possible values, and the formula is valid then too.

By definition,

$$\text{Var } (X) = E((x - \mu)^2) = (x_1 - \mu)^2 f(x_1)$$
$$+ (x_2 - \mu)^2 f(x_2) + (x_3 - \mu)^2 f(x_3),$$

where $\mu = E(X)$ and f is the probability function determined by X. If we perform the indicated squaring operations, we get

$$\text{Var } (X) = (x_1^2 - 2\mu x_1 + \mu^2) f(x_1) + (x_2^2 - 2\mu x_2 + \mu^2) f(x_2)$$
$$+ (x_3^2 - 2\mu x_3 + \mu^2) f(x_3).$$

Performing the indicated multiplications, and regrouping the terms we get

$$\text{Var } (X) = x_1^2 f(x_1) + x_2^2 f(x_2) + x_3^2 f(x_3)$$
$$- 2\mu[x_1 f(x_1) + x_2 f(x_2) + x_3 f(x_3)]$$
$$+ \mu^2[f(x_1) + f(x_2) + f(x_3)].$$

On the right-hand side of this equation, the expression on the first line is equal to $E(X^2)$. The expression in square brackets on the second line is equal to $E(X) = \mu$. The expression in square brackets on the third line is equal to 1. Making these substitutions, we have $\text{Var } (X) = E(X^2) - 2\mu^2 + \mu^2 = E(X^2) - \mu^2 = E(X^2) - [E(X)]^2$.

If we use this formula to compute the standard deviation of X, the computation follows this sequence of steps: First compute $E(X)$. Square each value of X. Then compute $E(X^2)$. Then find $\text{Var } (X)$, and take its square root to find σ. As an example, we use this procedure to find the standard deviation of the random variable $X =$ the number of heads when four fair coins are tossed. The first three columns of the table on the next page merely repeat the table that appears on page 134.

x	$f(x)$	$xf(x)$	x^2	$x^2f(x)$
0	$\frac{1}{16}$	0	0	0
1	$\frac{4}{16}$	$\frac{4}{16}$	1	$\frac{4}{16}$
2	$\frac{6}{16}$	$\frac{12}{16}$	4	$\frac{24}{16}$
3	$\frac{4}{16}$	$\frac{12}{16}$	9	$\frac{36}{16}$
4	$\frac{1}{16}$	$\frac{4}{16}$	16	$\frac{16}{16}$
Totals		$\frac{32}{16}$		$\frac{80}{16}$

$$E(X) = \tfrac{32}{16} = 2. \quad E(X^2) = \tfrac{80}{16} = 5.$$
$$\text{Var }(X) = E(X^2) - [E(X)]^2 = 5 - 4 = 1.$$
$$\sigma = \sqrt{\text{Var }(X)} = \sqrt{1} = 1.$$

The Variance and Standard Deviation of a Function of a Random Variable

Let X be a random variable over a sample space, and let Y be a real-valued function of X. Either the definition of Var (Y) or the formula, Var $(Y) = E(Y^2) - [E(Y)]^2$, permits us to calculate Var (Y), and then, by taking the square root, we find the standard deviation of Y. We carry these computations out for the variables $X + b$, aX, and $aX + b$. As before, we shall use the symbols μ and σ respectively to designate expectation and standard deviation. But now we must attach a subscript to each symbol to indicate which variable it belongs to. Thus μ_{X+b} stands for the expectation of $X + b$, and σ_{X+b} stands for its standard deviation.

The Variance and Standard Deviation of $X + b$. We note that $\mu_{X+b} = E(X + b) = E(X) + b = \mu_X + b$. By definition,

$$\begin{aligned}
\text{Var } (X + b) &= E([(X + b) - \mu_{X+b}]^2) \\
&= E([(X + b) - (\mu_X + b)]^2) \\
&= E((X - \mu_X)^2) = \text{Var } (X).
\end{aligned}$$

Therefore $\sigma_{X+b} = \sqrt{\text{Var } (X + b)} = \sqrt{\text{Var } (X)} = \sigma_X$. *That is, if a fixed number b is added to each value of a random variable X, the variance and the standard deviation of the variable remain unchanged.*

The Variance and Standard Deviation of aX. Var $(aX) = E((aX)^2) - [E(aX)]^2 = E(a^2X^2) - [E(aX)]^2$. But we know from the results of page 143 that $E(a^2X^2) = a^2E(X^2)$, and $E(aX) = aE(X)$. Making these substitutions, we have

$$\begin{aligned}
\text{Var } (aX) &= a^2E(X^2) - [aE(X)]^2 = a^2E(X^2) - a^2[E(X)]^2 \\
&= a^2(E(X^2) - [E(X)]^2) = a^2 \text{ Var } (X).
\end{aligned}$$

Consequently,

$$\begin{aligned}
\sigma_{aX} &= \sqrt{\text{Var } (aX)} = \sqrt{a^2 \text{ Var } (X)} \\
&= |a|\sqrt{\text{Var } (X)} = |a|\sigma_X,
\end{aligned}$$

where $|a|$, called the absolute value of a, is the positive number whose square is a^2. (If a is a positive number, $|a| = a$. If a is a negative number, then $|a| = -a$. For example, $|2| = 2$, and $|-2| = 2$.) Our conclusion then is that *if each value of a random variable is multiplied by a fixed number a, the variance of the variable is multiplied by a^2, and the standard deviation of the variable is multiplied by the positive number $|a|$.*

The Variance and Standard Deviation of $aX + b$. The two preceding results enable us to compute Var $(aX + b)$ and σ_{aX+b}. Var $(aX + b) = \text{Var } (aX) = a^2 \text{ Var } (X)$. $\sigma_{aX+b} = \sigma_{aX} = |a|\sigma_X$.

Standardized Variable

In the work of later chapters we shall have occasion to compare the probability function of one random variable with that of another. To permit a useful comparison, we shall first change each of the variables to new variables that have two properties in common: their expectations are zero, and their standard deviations are equal to 1. This change is easily accomplished with the help of the rules developed in this chapter. Let X be a random variable, with expectation μ_X and with standard deviation $\sigma_X \neq 0$. If we add $-\mu_X$ to each value of the variable, we obtain the variable $X - \mu_X$, whose expectation is 0, and whose standard deviation is equal to σ_X. If we multiply each value of this new variable by $1/\sigma_X$, we get a third variable, $\dfrac{X - \mu_X}{\sigma_X}$, whose expectation is 0 and whose standard deviation is 1. This third variable is generally denoted by X^*, and is called the *standardized random variable* obtained from X.

For example, let W be the random variable defined on page 130. We have found that $\mu_W = 72$, and $\sigma_W = 2.9$. Therefore the standardized variable $W^* = \dfrac{W - 72}{2.9}$.

The Probability of Values Near the Mean

An important question about any random variable X for which $\sigma_X \neq 0$ is this: What is the probability that values of the random variable are close to the mean or expected value? In order to give this question a precise meaning, it is necessary to say what we mean by *close*. We specify a degree of closeness to the mean value μ_X by choosing a positive number and requiring that the distance of x from μ_X should be less than or equal to that number if x is to qualify as being close to μ_X. This distance from x to μ_X is the absolute value of $x - \mu_X$, or $|x - \mu_X|$. The positive number we use to specify the upper limit that we impose on distances is usually expressed as a multiple of the standard deviation of the variable So the question, reformulated in order to make it precise, is this:

What is the probability that $|X - \mu_X|$ is less than or equal to $m\sigma_X$, where m is a positive number? In abbreviated form, we are asking "What is $P(|X - \mu_X| \leq m\sigma_X)$?" To visualize what this question means in terms of the graph of a probability function, imagine a vertical line drawn on the graph at a point that is a distance $m\sigma_X$ to the left of the mean, and another vertical line drawn at the point that is a distance $m\sigma_X$ to the right of the mean. These two points are $\mu_X - m\sigma_X$ and $\mu_X + m\sigma_X$. Our question asks, "What is the probability that a value of X falls on or between these two vertical lines?", or, "What is the probability that $\mu_X - m\sigma_X \leq x \leq \mu_X + m\sigma_X$?" This question is answered by a formula known as *Chebyshev's Inequality*, which we now derive.

Let $x_1, x_2, \ldots, x_k$ be the possible values of X. Only some of them satisfy the requirement that $|X - \mu_X| \leq m\sigma_X$. Suppose there are n values of X that satisfy this requirement. Let us renumber the values of X so that these n values are written first as $x_1, x_2, \ldots, x_n$, and the rest have the higher subscripts from $n + 1$ to k. The values $x_{n+1}, \ldots, x_k$ are all the values of X that satisfy the condition $|X - \mu_X| > m\sigma_X$. Consequently $P(|X - \mu_X| > m\sigma_X) = f(x_{n+1}) + \ldots + f(x_k)$. We derive Chebyshev's Inequality from the definition of variance as follows:

$$\sigma_X^2 = \text{Var}\,(X) = E((X - \mu_X)^2). \text{ Therefore}$$
$$\sigma_X^2 = (x_1 - \mu_X)^2 f(x_1) + \ldots + (x_n - \mu_X)^2 f(x_n)$$
$$+ (x_{n+1} - \mu_X)^2 f(x_{n+1}) \ldots + (x_k - \mu_X)^2 f(x_k).$$

We now modify the right-hand side of the last equation as follows: In the first line replace each term by 0. In the second line, replace each $x_i - \mu_X$ by $m\sigma_X$, for $i = n + 1, \ldots, k$. Since each term is replaced in this way by a number that is no larger than the original term, but may perhaps be smaller, we then have that the left hand side of the equation is greater than or equal to the modified right hand side:

$$\sigma_X^2 \geqq (m\sigma_X)^2 f(x_{n+1}) + \ldots + (m\sigma_X)^2 f(x_k), \text{ or}$$
$$\sigma_X^2 \geqq m^2\sigma_X^2(f(x_{n+1}) + \ldots + f(x_k)), \text{ or}$$
$$\sigma_X^2 \geq m^2\sigma_X^2 P(|X - \mu_X| > m\sigma_X).$$

Dividing through by the positive number $m^2\sigma_X^2$, and reading the resulting inequality backwards, we get

$$P(|X - \mu_X| > m\sigma_X) \leq \frac{1}{m^2}.$$

The event that $|X - \mu_X| \leqq m\sigma_X$ is the complement of the event that $|X - \mu_X| > m\sigma_X$. Consequently

$$P(|X - \mu_X| \leqq m\sigma_X) \geqq 1 - \frac{1}{m^2}.$$

The last inequality is the one that answers the question with which we opened this paragraph.

If $m = 2$, Chebyshev's Inequality asserts that the probability that a random variable has a value that is within 2 standard deviations of its mean value is over $\frac{3}{4}$. Notice that this assertion is made for all random variables without exception. We shall find later, that for particular classes of random variables an even stronger assertion can be made.

Let us see what prediction Chebyshev's Inequality makes for the random variable W defined on page 130, with $m = 2$. We found that $\mu_W = 72$, and $\sigma_W = 2.9$. So Chebyshev's Inequality predicts that the probability that W is between 66.2 and 77.8 inclusive is at least .75. Examination of the table on page 130 shows that this probability is actually .96. (Add all entries except the last two in column 2.) The Chebyshev prediction turns out to be a very cautious one in this case.

Exercises for Chapter VI

1. Three fair coins are tossed independently. Use the appropriate 8-element sample space. Let $X =$ the number of

heads that turn up. Construct 1) a table showing the value of X associated with each possible outcome of the experiment; 2) a table listing all possible values of X, the corresponding events in the sample space, and the probabilities of these events; 3) a table showing $f(x) = P(X = x)$ for all possible values of X; 4) a graph of $f(x)$.

2. In a year that is not a leap year, a month is chosen at random. Let the random variable X = the number of days in the month. Construct a table showing $f(x) = P(X = x)$ for all possible values of X.

3. Find the expectation of the random variable defined in exercise 1.

4. Find the expectation of the random variable defined in exercise 2.

5. Four cards are numbered from 1 to 4. The cards are shuffled and then turned over one at a time. We say a match occurs if the n'th card turned over has the number n on it, for $n = 1, 2, 3, 4$. Let X = the number of matches that occur. Construct a table for the probability function determined by X. What is the expected number of matches?

6. On a test given in an English class, four words were printed in a column, and the definitions of the four words were printed in an arbitrary order in an adjoining column. The student was asked to pick out the correct definition for each word. The score given for the answer was the number of words correctly defined minus the number of words incorrectly defined. If a student guesses the answers, what is his expected score?

7. For the blood test described on page 136, suppose 1% of all blood samples taken from a particular population have a positive reaction. For a mass test of this population, how many samples should be pooled for the expected per cent of saving to be a maximum?

8. Using the random variable W defined on page 130, find $E(W - 72)$ and $E(2W)$.

9. Defining W as in exercise 8, compute σ_W by means of the formula $\text{Var}(W) = E(W^2) - [E(W)]^2$.

10. Using the random variable X defined in exercise 1, compute σ_X.

11. Using the random variable X defined in exercise 5, compute σ_X.

12. Using the random variables Y and Z defined on page 125, compute σ_Y and σ_Z.

13. Using X, Y and Z as defined on page 125, find the standardized random variables X^*, Y^*, and Z^*.

CHAPTER VII

Correlation

Linked Random Variables

WE OFTEN encounter statements such as these: The more years of schooling a person has, the higher his income as an adult is likely to be. The more rainfall there is during a year, the wider the growth-ring of a tree is likely to be for that year. The higher the level of unemployment, the higher the crime rate is. But the higher the level of unemployment, the lower the rate of juvenile delinquency is. Each of these statements concerns two random variables, and asserts that there is a connection or linkage between the two. The statements indicate, too, that the linkage is of a special kind known as *correlation*. The purpose of this chapter is to formulate the concept of correlation precisely, so that we may have a better understanding of what statements like these mean.

Many Random Variables Over One Sample Space

It is possible to have many random variables defined over the same sample space. As a concrete example, consider the experiment of tossing a fair coin three times. Use as sample space the set

$$S = \{HHH, HHT, HTH, THH, HTT, THT, TTH, TTT\}$$

whose simple events all have probability $\frac{1}{8}$. We define six separate random variables, X, Y, Z, U, V and W as follows:

X = the total gain of a player who is paid \$3 if the coin falls *heads* on the first toss, an additional \$2 if it falls *heads* on the second toss, and an additional \$1 if it falls *heads* on the third toss;

Y = the number of heads obtained;

Z = the number of tails obtained;

U = a variable that has only two possible values, 0 and 1: it is 0 if the coin falls *tails* on the first toss, and it is 1 if the coin falls *heads* on the first toss;

V = 0 if the coin falls *tails* on the second toss, and it is 1 if the coin falls *heads* on the second toss.

W = 0 if the coin falls *tails* on the third toss, and it is 1 if the coin falls *heads* on the third toss.

The table below lists the elements of S and the corresponding values of each of these variables.

Outcome	x	y	z	u	v	w
HHH	6	3	0	1	1	1
HHT	5	2	1	1	1	0
HTH	4	2	1	1	0	1
THH	3	2	1	0	1	1
HTT	3	1	2	1	0	0
THT	2	1	2	0	1	0
TTH	1	1	2	0	0	1
TTT	0	0	3	0	0	0

To look for relationships among the variables, we examine a pair of them at a time. The first step in this examination is to list the possible values of the pair, and then determine for each value the probability of the event that that value occurs.

Let us consider first the ordered pair of random variables, (X, Y). The possible values of X constitute the set $\{0, 1, 2, 3, 4, 5, 6\}$. The possible values of Y constitute the set $\{0, 1, 2, 3\}$. Then the possible values of (X, Y) are ordered pairs that are elements of the Cartesian product of these two sets. For example, one of these possible values is the ordered pair $(3, 1)$. The event that $(X, Y) = (3, 1)$ is the event that $X = 3$ *and* $Y = 1$. To designate this event, we shall write $(X = 3, Y = 1)$, using a comma instead of the word *and*. From the table above we see that $X = 3$ describes the event $\{THH, HTT\}$, and $Y = 1$ describes the event $\{HTT, THT, TTH\}$. $(X = 3, Y = 1)$ is the intersection of these two events, so it is the event $\{HTT\}$, and the probability of this event is $\frac{1}{8}$. Similarly, for each ordered pair of real numbers, (x, y), the event $(X = x, Y = y)$ is the intersection of the event $X = x$ with the event $Y = y$, and its membership and probability can be determined from the table. If the intersection is the empty set, then its probability, of course, is 0. The information obtained in this way is recorded in a *joint probability table* for the pair of random variables (X, Y). In this table, shown below, the possible values of X are written at the left, and the possible values of Y are written at the top. A horizontal row corresponds to each possible value of X. A vertical column corresponds to each possible value of Y. A cell which is the intersection of a particular

X \ Y	0	1	2	3	$P(X = x)$
0	$\frac{1}{8}$	0	0	0	$\frac{1}{8}$
1	0	$\frac{1}{8}$	0	0	$\frac{1}{8}$
2	0	$\frac{1}{8}$	0	0	$\frac{1}{8}$
3	0	$\frac{1}{8}$	$\frac{1}{8}$	0	$\frac{2}{8}$
4	0	0	$\frac{1}{8}$	0	$\frac{1}{8}$
5	0	0	$\frac{1}{8}$	0	$\frac{1}{8}$
6	0	0	0	$\frac{1}{8}$	$\frac{1}{8}$
$P(Y = y)$	$\frac{1}{8}$	$\frac{3}{8}$	$\frac{3}{8}$	$\frac{1}{8}$	1

row and column corresponds to the event (X = the number to the left of the row, Y = the number at the top of the column). The number written in the cell is the probability of that event. Notice that some of the cells contain the number 0. This means that the event represented by each of these cells is the empty set. Any ordered pair (x, y) that is not represented by a cell in the table also corresponds to the empty set, and hence also has associated with it the probability 0. For example, the probability of the event (X = 7, Y = 1) is 0.

After all the cells have been filled in, we may, if we wish, disregard the original sample space, and consider the set of cells as a sample space whose simple events have the probabilities written in the cells. With this assignment of probabilities the table itself becomes a legitimate probability model satisfying all the requirements listed on page 36. You will notice that one of the requirements was that the probability of each simple event should be a *non-negative* number. We deliberately said *non-negative* rather than *positive* in order to permit us to have simple events with probability 0, as we do here.

If we think of the set of cells (or the ordered pairs they represent) as the sample space, then the event X = 0 is the union of the simple events represented by the cells in the row that is labeled X = 0. Then $P(X = 0)$ is the sum of the probabilities in these cells. Similarly, for each possible value x of X, $P(X = x)$ is the sum of the probabilities written in the cells of the corresponding row. These probabilities are written at the right-hand end of the table, and show the values of the probability function of the random variable X for the values of X listed at the left. In the same way, for each possible value y of Y, $P(Y = y)$ is the sum of the probabilities written in the cells of the corresponding column. These probabilities are written at the bottom of the table, and show the values of the probability function of the random variable Y for the values of Y listed at the top. The numbers $P(X = x)$ and

$P(Y = y)$ are called the *marginal* probabilities of the table, since they appear in the right and bottom margins. The number 1, written in the lower right hand corner of the table, is the sum of all the possible values of $P(X = x)$, and also the sum of all the possible values of $P(Y = y)$, as we would expect.

The joint probability tables for the pairs of random variables (Y, Z) and (U, V) are constructed in the same way and are shown below. The reader can verify the probabilities shown in these tables by consulting the table on page 155 which shows the value of each of the random variables for each possible outcome of the experiment of tossing a coin three times.

Y \ Z	0	1	2	3	$P(Y = y)$
0	0	0	0	$\frac{1}{8}$	$\frac{1}{8}$
1	0	0	$\frac{3}{8}$	0	$\frac{3}{8}$
2	0	$\frac{3}{8}$	0	0	$\frac{3}{8}$
3	$\frac{1}{8}$	0	0	0	$\frac{1}{8}$
$P(Z = z)$	$\frac{1}{8}$	$\frac{3}{8}$	$\frac{3}{8}$	$\frac{1}{8}$	1

U \ V	0	1	$P(U = u)$
0	$\frac{1}{4}$	$\frac{1}{4}$	$\frac{1}{2}$
1	$\frac{1}{4}$	$\frac{1}{4}$	$\frac{1}{2}$
$P(V = v)$	$\frac{1}{2}$	$\frac{1}{2}$	1

Independent Random Variables

On page 114 we established a criterion for *independent events:* Two events E and F are independent if $P(E \cap F) = P(E)P(F)$. Let us apply this criterion to some of the events listed in the joint probability table for the pair (X, Y). For the event E choose the event $X = 3$. Its probability is $\frac{2}{8}$. For the event F choose the event $Y = 1$. Its probability is $\frac{3}{8}$. These two events are independent if and only if the probability of their intersection satisfies the multiplication rule, that is, if and only if $P(X = 3, Y = 1)$ is $\frac{2}{8} \times \frac{3}{8}$, or $\frac{6}{64}$. However, $P(X = 3, Y = 1)$ is shown in the corresponding cell, and it is equal to $\frac{1}{8}$. So it does not follow the multiplication rule, and the two events $X = 3$ and $Y = 1$ are *not* independent. Similarly, the table shows that for all values x of X and y of Y shown in the table, the events $X = x$ and $Y = y$ are not independent.

We find a different situation, however, in the joint probability table for the pair (U, V). There we find that $P(U = 0) = \frac{1}{2}$, $P(V = 0) = \frac{1}{2}$, and $P(U = 0, V = 0) = \frac{1}{4}$, so that the multiplication rule is satisfied. Consequently the events $U = 0$ and $V = 0$ are independent. Similarly, $U = 0$ and $V = 1$ are independent, $U = 1$ and $V = 0$ are independent, and $U = 1$ and $V = 1$ are independent. In a situation like this one, we say that the two variables U and V are independent, in accordance with the following definition: *Two random variables X and Y are independent if, for all possible values x of X and y of Y the events X = x and Y = y are independent.* The multiplication rule for independent events gives us a simple way of recognizing independent random variables. Two random variables X and Y are independent if and only if each entry in a cell of the joint probability table for the pair (X, Y) is the product of the corresponding marginal probabilities. Random variables that are not independent are called *dependent*. With X, Y and Z defined as on page 155, the variables X and Y are dependent, and so are Y and Z.

The definition of independent random variables is easily extended to three or more variables: Let $X_1, X_2, \ldots, X_n$ be n random variables over the same sample space. They are independent if, for all possible values x_1 of X_1, x_2 of X_2, and so on, the events $X_1 = x_1, X_2 = x_2, \ldots, X_n = x_n$ are independent events. Independent random variables are characterized by the multiplication rule

$$P(X_1 = x_1, X_2 = x_2, \ldots, X_n = x_n)$$
$$= P(X_1 = x_1)P(X_2 = x_2) \ldots P(X_n = x_n).$$

Functions of Independent Random Variables

Let $X_1, X_2, \ldots, X_n$ be independent random variables. Suppose Y_1 is a real-valued function of X_1, Y_2 is a real-valued function of X_2, and so on. Then it is not difficult to show that $Y_1, Y_2, \ldots, Y_n$ are also independent random variables. We shall not prove this assertion here. However, the exercises at the end of the chapter will give the reader some opportunities to verify the assertion in some particular cases.

Variables that Depend on One Trial Only

The experiment of tossing a fair coin three times, with each possible outcome assigned the probability $\frac{1}{8}$, is an example of a compound experiment made up of independent trials. (See the definition on page 119.) The random variable U, defined on page 155, depends only on the first trial, the random variable V depends only on the second trial, and the random variable W depends only on the third trial. It is easy to verify that for all possible values u of U, v of V, and w of W, $P(U = u, V = v, W = w) = P(U = u)P(V = v)P(W = w)$, so that U, V, and W are independent random variables. This fact is an example of a more general rule: If an experiment is made up of n independent trials, where n is an integer that is greater than 1, and if X_1 is a random variable that depends only on the first trial, X_2 is a random variable that depends only on the second trial, and so on, then $X_1, X_2, \ldots X_n$ are independent random variables. We shall have occasion to use this rule in the next chapter.

Sum and Product

Let X and Y be the random variables shown in the table on page 155. Then $X + Y$ and XY are also random variables over the same sample space for which X and Y are defined. The values of $X + Y$ and XY for each possible outcome in the sample space are shown in the table below. They are obtained by adding and multiplying, respectively the corresponding values of X and Y.

Outcome	x	y	$x + y$	xy
HHH	6	3	9	18
HHT	5	2	7	10
HTH	4	2	6	8
THH	3	2	5	6
HTT	3	1	4	3
THT	2	1	3	2
TTH	1	1	2	1
TTT	0	0	0	0

From this table we get all the information that we need to construct the tables for the probability functions of $X + Y$ and XY. We keep in mind, of course, that the probability of each simple event in the sample space is $\frac{1}{8}$. The resulting tables are shown below:

$x + y$	0	1	2	3	4	5	6	7	8	9
$P(X + Y = n)$	$\frac{1}{8}$	0	$\frac{1}{8}$	$\frac{1}{8}$	$\frac{1}{8}$	$\frac{1}{8}$	$\frac{1}{8}$	$\frac{1}{8}$	0	$\frac{1}{8}$

xy	0	1	2	3	4	5	6	7	8	9
$P(XY = n)$	$\frac{1}{8}$	$\frac{1}{8}$	$\frac{1}{8}$	$\frac{1}{8}$	0	0	$\frac{1}{8}$	0	$\frac{1}{8}$	0

xy	10	11	12	13	14	15	16	17	18
$P(XY = n)$	$\frac{1}{8}$	0	0	0	0	0	0	0	$\frac{1}{8}$

Using these tables, we can compute the expectation of $X + Y$ and of XY. We recall that to compute the expectation of a random variable we multiply each possible value of the variable by the probability that it occurs, and then add all the products. We may pass over those values of the variable that have probability 0, since they contribute 0 to the sum.

Then $E(X + Y) = 0(\frac{1}{8}) + 2(\frac{1}{8}) + 3(\frac{1}{8}) + 4(\frac{1}{8}) + 5(\frac{1}{8})$
$$+ 6(\frac{1}{8}) + 7(\frac{1}{8}) + 9(\frac{1}{8}) = 4.5.$$
$$E(XY) = 0(\frac{1}{8}) + 1(\frac{1}{8}) + 2(\frac{1}{8}) + 3(\frac{1}{8}) + 6(\frac{1}{8})$$
$$+ 8(\frac{1}{8}) + 10(\frac{1}{8}) + 18(\frac{1}{8}) = 6.$$

There is another way of computing the expectation of $X + Y$ and XY *without first constructing the tables for their probability functions.* We work instead with the joint probability table of (X, Y). To find the expectation of $X + Y$, proceed as follows: For each possible ordered pair (x, y), find the corresponding value of $X + Y$, namely $x + y$, and multiply it by $P(X = x, Y = y)$, which is the number in the corresponding cell. Then add all the products. You may pass over those cells for which the probability is 0. This procedure is analogous to the one developed on page 141 for a function of a single random variable, and may be justified by an argument like the one that is used there.

Computing $E(X + Y)$ by this new procedure, we find that

$$E(X + Y) = (0 + 0)(\frac{1}{8}) + (1 + 1)(\frac{1}{8}) + (2 + 1)(\frac{1}{8})$$
$$+ (3 + 1)(\frac{1}{8}) + (3 + 2)(\frac{1}{8}) + (4 + 2)(\frac{1}{8})$$
$$+ (5 + 2)(\frac{1}{8}) + (6 + 3)(\frac{1}{8}) = 4.5.$$

Computing $E(XY)$ by the same method, we find that

$$E(XY) = (0 \times 0)(\frac{1}{8}) + (1 \times 1)(\frac{1}{8}) + (2 \times 1)(\frac{1}{8})$$
$$+ (3 \times 1)(\frac{1}{8}) + (3 \times 2)(\frac{1}{8}) + (4 \times 2)(\frac{1}{8})$$
$$+ (5 \times 2)(\frac{1}{8}) + (6 \times 3)(\frac{1}{8}) = 6.$$

It is instructive to compare these expectations with $E(X)$ and $E(Y)$. $E(X) = 6(\frac{1}{8}) + 5(\frac{1}{8}) + 4(\frac{1}{8}) + 3(\frac{2}{8}) + 2(\frac{1}{8}) + 1(\frac{1}{8}) + 0(\frac{1}{8}) = 3$. $E(Y) = 3(\frac{1}{8}) + 2(\frac{3}{8}) + 1(\frac{3}{8}) +$

$0(\frac{1}{8}) = 1.5$. We observe that $E(X + Y) = E(X) + E(Y)$, but $E(XY)$ is not equal to $E(X)E(Y)$.

Expectation of a Sum of Random Variables

We observed in the preceding paragraph that, with X and Y as defined on page 155, $E(X + Y) = E(X) + E(Y)$. This result is not exceptional, but is true for any two random variables X and Y defined over the same sample space. To show the method used for proving this statement we shall carry through the proof in the case where X has only two possible values, x_1, x_2, and Y has only three possible values, y_1, y_2, y_3. It will be clear that the same method can be used in other cases as well.

We first define three probability functions f, g, and h as follows: $f(x) = P(X = x)$; $g(y) = P(Y = y)$; $h(x, y) = p(X = x, Y = y)$. Then the joint probability table for (X, Y) takes this form:

X \ Y	y_1	y_2	y_3	$P(X = x)$
x_1	$h(x_1, y_1)$	$h(x_1, y_2)$	$h(x_1, y_3)$	$f(x_1)$
x_2	$h(x_2, y_1)$	$h(x_2, y_2)$	$h(x_2, y_3)$	$f(x_2)$
$P(Y = y)$	$g(y_1)$	$g(y_2)$	$g(y_3)$	1

Using the second method for computing $E(X + Y)$, we find that

$$
\begin{aligned}
E(X + Y) = {}& (x_1 + y_1)h(x_1, y_1) + (x_1 + y_2)h(x_1, y_2) \\
& + (x_1 + y_3)h(x_1, y_3) + (x_2 + y_1)h(x_2, y_1) \\
& + (x_2 + y_2)h(x_2, y_2) + (x_2 + y_3)h(x_2, y_3).
\end{aligned}
$$

If we perform the indicated multiplications, and then re-
group the terms, we find that

$$E(X + Y) = x_1(h(x_1, y_1) + h(x_1, y_2) + h(x_1, y_3))$$
$$+ x_2(h(x_2, y_1) + h(x_2, y_2) + h(x_2, y_3))$$
$$+ y_1(h(x_1, y_1) + h(x_2, y_1))$$
$$+ y_2(h(x_1, y_2) + h(x_2, y_2))$$
$$+ y_3(h(x_1, y_3) + h(x_2, y_3)).$$

In this equation, the coefficient of x_1 is the sum of the
entries in the cells of the x_1 row in the table. This sum is
equal to the marginal probability $f(x_1)$. Similarly, the coefficient of x_2 is equal to $f(x_2)$. The coefficient of y_1 is the
sum of the entries in the cells of the y_1 column. This sum
is equal to the marginal probability $g(y_1)$. Similarly, the
coefficient of y_2 is equal to $g(y_2)$, and the coefficient of y_3
is equal to $g(y_3)$. Making these substitutions, we find that

$$E(X + Y) = x_1f(x_1) + x_2f(x_2) + y_1g(y_1)$$
$$+ y_2g(y_2) + y_3g(y_3)$$
$$= E(X) + E(Y).$$

Consequently, the expectation of the sum of two random
variables over a sample space is the sum of their expectations.

By using this rule twice, we can extend the result to
three random variables. Suppose X_1, X_2, and X_3 are random variables defined over the same sample space. Then

$$E(X_1 + X_2 + X_3) = E(X_1 + (X_2 + X_3)) = E(X_1)$$
$$+ E(X_2 + X_3) = E(X_1) + E(X_2) + E(X_3).$$

Following a step by step procedure, we can also extend the
result to four random variables, five random variables,
and so on. Consequently we have this general result: If n
is a positive integer greater than 1, and $X_1, X_2, \ldots, X_n$
are random variables over the same sample space, then

$$(1) \quad E(X_1 + X_2 + \ldots + X_n)$$
$$= E(X_1) + E(X_2) + \ldots + E(X_n).$$

By invoking the rule $E(aX) = aE(X)$, established in the preceding chapter, we make one more extension of our result to obtain an equation that we shall have to use later: Let $X_1, X_2, \ldots, X_n$ be random variables over the same sample space, and let $a_1, a_2, \ldots, a_n$ be real numbers. Then $a_1X_1 + a_2X_2 + \ldots + a_nX_n$ is a random variable over the same sample space, and

$$
\begin{aligned}
(2) \quad E(a_1X_1 &+ a_2X_2 + \ldots + a_nX_n) \\
&= E(a_1X_1) + E(a_2X_2) + \ldots + E(a_nX_n) \\
&= a_1E(X_1) + a_2E(X_2) + \ldots + a_nE(X_n).
\end{aligned}
$$

Covariance of Two Random Variables

While the expectation of the sum of two random variables is equal to the sum of their expectations, the expectation of their product need not be the product of their expectations. We know this to be so, because we have already observed a case where $E(XY) \neq E(X)E(Y)$. Since $E(XY)$ and $E(X)E(Y)$ may differ, let us give a name to their difference, and see what information it gives us about the relationship between X and Y. We call $E(XY) - E(X)E(Y)$ the *covariance* of X and Y, and denote it by Cov (X, Y). Since $E(X)$ is also designated by μ_X, and $E(Y)$ is designated by μ_Y, we may also write:

$$
(3) \qquad \text{Cov } (X, Y) = E(XY) - \mu_X\mu_Y.
$$

First we derive an equivalent expression for Cov (X, Y) that will be useful. To find $E[(X - \mu_X)(Y - \mu_Y)]$, we perform the indicated multiplication inside the square brackets. Then

$$
\begin{aligned}
E[(X - \mu_X)(Y - \mu_Y)] &= E(XY - \mu_XY - \mu_YX + \mu_X\mu_Y) \\
&= E(XY - \mu_XY - \mu_YX) + \mu_X\mu_Y,
\end{aligned}
$$

according to equation (3) of page 142. Applying equation (2) of page 165 to this last expression, we find that $E[(X - \mu_X)(Y - \mu_Y)] = E(XY) - \mu_XE(Y) - \mu_YE(X) +$

$\mu_X\mu_Y$. But $E(X) = \mu_X$, and $E(Y) = \mu_Y$. Making these substitutions and combining like terms, we find that $E[(X - \mu_X)(Y - \mu_Y)] = E(XY) - \mu_X\mu_Y$, which is equal to Cov (X, Y). Consequently,

(4) $\qquad$ Cov $(X, Y) = E[(X - \mu_X)(Y - \mu_Y)]$.

We find a third expression for Cov (X, Y) by evaluating Cov $(X - \mu_X, Y - \mu_Y)$. If, in equation (3), we replace X by $X - \mu_X$, and replace Y by $Y - \mu_Y$, we get

$$\text{Cov } (X - \mu_X, Y - \mu_Y) = E[(X - \mu_X)(Y - \mu_Y)] - (\mu_{X-\mu_X})(\mu_{Y-\mu_Y}).$$

But $\mu_{X-\mu_X} = E(X - \mu_X) = 0$, and $\mu_{Y-\mu_Y} = E(Y - \mu_Y) = 0$. So

$$\text{Cov } (X - \mu_X, Y - \mu_Y) = E[(X - \mu_X)(Y - \mu_Y)].$$

Then, in view of equation (4), we have

(5) $\qquad$ Cov $(X - \mu_X, Y - \mu_Y) = \text{cov } (X, Y)$.

A Measure of Correlation

Equation (4) expresses Cov (X, Y) as the expectation of the random variable $(X - \mu_X)(Y - \mu_Y)$. By examining this expectation, we get clues to the behavior of X and Y with respect to each other. To find these clues, let us note first that if a random variable is not constant, and its possible values that differ from zero are all positive, then its average is positive. Similarly, if a random variable is not constant, and its possible values that differ from zero are all negative, then its average is negative.

To examine the behavior of the variables X and Y, we consider pairs of values (x, y) that are associated with the same element of the sample space. We shall call these *corresponding* values. Suppose X and Y have the property that, when they are not equal to their respective averages, corresponding values of X and Y are either both above average together, or both below average together. Then $X - \mu_X$ and $Y - \mu_Y$, when they are not equal to zero, are either both positive or both negative for corresponding pairs of values (x, y). Consequently their product, when it is not zero, is always positive, and the expectation of their product, which is equal to Cov (X, Y), is also positive. Suppose, on the other hand, X and Y have the property that above-average values of X correspond to below-average values of Y, and vice versa. Then $X - \mu_X$ and $Y - \mu_Y$, when they are not both zero, have opposite signs. Then their product, when it is not zero, is always negative, and the expectation of their product, which is equal to Cov (X, Y), is also negative. In short, when corresponding values of X and Y deviate from their averages in the same direction, Cov (X, Y) is positive. When they deviate from their averages in opposite directions, Cov (X, Y) is negative. This suggests using Cov (X, Y) as a measure of how the deviation of X and the deviation of Y are related to each other. In order to standardize the measure, we shall use instead, however, Cov (X^*, Y^*), where X^* and Y^* are the standardized random variables derived from X and Y. We recall from page 149 that X^* and Y^* are defined only if $\sigma_X \neq 0$ and $\sigma_Y \neq 0$. These considerations are the basis of the following definition. Let X and Y be random variables over the sample space. The *correlation coefficient of X and Y* is denoted by $\rho(X, Y)$ and is defined as follows:

(6) $\quad \begin{cases} \text{If } \sigma_X = 0, \text{ or } \sigma_Y = 0, \rho(X, Y) = 0. \\ \text{If } \sigma_X \neq 0, \text{ and } \sigma_Y \neq 0, \rho(X, Y) = \text{Cov } (X^*, Y^*). \end{cases}$

If $\rho(X, Y) \neq 0$, we say that X and Y are *correlated*. If $\rho(X, Y) = 0$, we say that X and Y are *uncorrelated*.

For computational purposes we shall find it convenient to express $\rho(X, Y)$ in terms of X and Y rather than in terms of X^* and Y^*. If $\sigma_X \neq 0$ and $\sigma_Y \neq 0$, we have

(7) $\rho(X, Y) = \text{Cov}(X^*, Y^*) = E(X^*Y^*) - \mu_{X^*}\mu_{Y^*}$

$$= E(X^*Y^*) = E\left(\frac{(X - \mu_X)}{\sigma_X} \cdot \frac{(Y - \mu_Y)}{\sigma_Y}\right)$$

$$= \frac{E[(X - \mu_X)(Y - \mu_Y)]}{\sigma_X\sigma_Y} = \frac{\text{Cov}(X, Y)}{\sigma_X\sigma_Y}.$$

To illustrate the use of this formula, we compute the correlation coefficient of the random variables X and Y defined on page 155. We have already found that $E(XY) = 6$, $\mu_X = E(X) = 3$, and $\mu_Y = E(Y) = 1.5$. Therefore

Cov $(X, Y) = E(XY) - \mu_X\mu_Y = 1.5$.
$E(X^2) = \frac{1}{8}(36 + 25 + 16 + 9 + 9 + 4 + 1) = 12.5$.

Then Var $(X) = E(X^2) - [E(X)]^2 = 12.5 - 9 = 3.5$, and $\sigma_X = \sqrt{3.5}$. $E(Y^2) = \frac{1}{8}(9 + 4 + 4 + 4 + 1 + 1 + 1) = 3$. Var $(Y) = E(Y^2) - [E(Y)]^2 = 3 - 2.25 = .75$, and $\sigma_Y = \sqrt{.75}$. Then $\rho(X, Y) = \dfrac{1.5}{\sqrt{3.5}\sqrt{.75}} = .93$, approximately.

Possible Values of the Correlation Coefficient

In order to find the range of possible values of $\rho(X, Y)$, we first derive a formula for Var $(X + Y)$. From the definition of variance, Var $(X + Y)$ is the average of the square of the deviation of $X + Y$. So we obtain our result by a sequence of three steps: first find the deviation of $X + Y$, then square it, and then find the average of the square of the deviation. The deviation of $X + Y$ is $X + Y - E(X + Y) = X + Y - E(X) - E(Y) = X + Y - \mu_X - \mu_Y = (X - \mu_X) + (Y - \mu_Y)$. Squaring this expression, we get

$$(X - \mu_X)^2 + (Y - \mu_Y)^2 + 2(X - \mu_X)(Y - \mu_Y).$$

Taking the average of the latter expression we get

$$E[(X - \mu_X)^2 + (Y - \mu_Y)^2 + 2(X - \mu_X)(Y - \mu_Y)]$$
$$= E[(X - \mu_X)^2] + E[(Y - \mu_Y)^2]$$
$$+ 2E[(X - \mu_X)(Y - \mu_Y)].$$

But $E[(X - \mu_X)^2] = \text{Var}(X)$, $E[(Y - \mu_Y)^2] = \text{Var}(Y)$, and $E[(X - \mu_X)(Y - \mu_Y)] = \text{Cov}(X, Y)$. So we have this formula:

(8) $\text{Var}(X + Y) = \text{Var}(X) + \text{Var}(Y) + 2\,\text{Cov}(X, Y)$.

Using this formula with the standardized variables X^* and Y^* we get $\text{Var}(X^* + Y^*) = \text{Var}(X^*) + \text{Var}(Y^*) + 2\,\text{Cov}(X^*, Y^*)$. But $\text{Var}(X^*) = 1$, $\text{Var}(Y^*) = 1$, and $\text{Cov}(X^*, Y^*) = \rho(X, Y)$. Consequently $\text{Var}(X^* + Y^*) = 2(1 + \rho(X, Y))$. From the definition of variance we know that $\text{Var}(X^* + Y^*)$ cannot be negative. Therefore $1 + \rho(X, Y)$ cannot be negative, and $\rho(X, Y)$ must be greater than or equal to -1. By first deriving a formula for $\text{Var}(X - Y)$, we can show in the same way that

$$\text{Var}(X^* - Y^*) = 2(1 - \rho(X, Y)).$$

Then, since $\text{Var}(X^* - Y^*)$ cannot be negative, $1 - \rho(X, Y)$ cannot be negative, and $\rho(X, Y)$ must be less than or equal to 1. Consequently $\rho(X, Y)$ is a number between -1 and 1 inclusive.

The Ultimate of Correlation

The absolute value of the correlation coefficient for two random variables indicates how strongly correlated they are. Its maximum possible value is 1, and occurs when $\rho(X, Y)$ has one of the extreme values, 1 or -1. To get an intuitive picture of what a correlation coefficient signifies, let us investigate first the meaning of these extreme cases.

How are X and Y related to each other if $\rho(X, Y) = 1$? To answer this question, let us recall first that each of the random variables X and Y assigns a definite value, x and y, to each element of the sample space over which the variables are defined. It is possible that some of the simple events in the sample space have probability 0. Let us exclude these from consideration, because a value of a variable that occurs with probability 0 is not a *possible* value, and therefore need not concern us.

We saw in the preceding section that Var $(X^* - Y^*) = 2(1 - \rho(X, Y))$. If $\rho(X, Y) = 1$, it follows that Var $(X^* - Y^*) = 0$. If the variance of a random variable is 0, it means that the deviation of each *possible* value is 0. That is, no *possible* values of the variable differ from its mean. Consequently, for *possible* values, $X^* - Y^* = E(X^* - Y^*)$. But $E(X^* - Y^*) = E(X^*) - E(Y^*) = 0 - 0 = 0$. Therefore for all *possible* values of X and Y, $X^* - Y^* = 0$, or $X^* = Y^*$. Keeping in mind the definition of a standardized random variable, we see then that

$$\frac{X - \mu_X}{\sigma_X} = \frac{Y - \mu_Y}{\sigma_Y}.$$

Solving this equation for Y in terms of X, we find that

$$Y = \left(\frac{\sigma_Y}{\sigma_X}\right) X + \frac{\sigma_X \mu_Y - \sigma_Y \mu_X}{\sigma_X}$$

This equation has the form $Y = mX + b$, where $m = \dfrac{\sigma_Y}{\sigma_X}$. Moreover, since $\rho(X, Y) = 1$, σ_X and σ_Y are both not O and hence both are positive. Therefore, m is a positive number. The reader will recall from high school algebra that if $Y = mX + b$, the variables X and Y are linearly related, that is, the graph of the equation $Y = mX + b$ is a straight line. The fact that m is positive indicates that the straight line slopes up to the right. This signifies that as X increases, Y also increases.

If $\rho(X, Y) = -1$, begin with the equation

$$\text{Var } (X* + Y*) = 2(1 + \rho(X, Y)).$$

A similar argument will then show that X and Y are related by an equation of the form $Y = mX + b$ where m is negative. Again the graph of the equation is a straight line. The fact that m is negative indicates that the straight line slopes down to the right. This signifies that as X increases, Y decreases.

We have shown that if $\rho(X, Y) = 1$ or -1, then for possible values of X and Y, $Y = mX + b$, where $m \neq 0$. We now prove the converse. Suppose $Y = mX + b$, and $m \neq 0$. Cov $(X, Y) = E[(X - \mu_X)(Y - \mu_Y)]$. Since $Y = mX + b$, we have $\mu_Y = m\mu_X + b$. Consequently $Y - \mu_Y = m(X - \mu_X)$. Making this substitution, we get Cov $(X, Y) = E[m(X - \mu_X)^2] = mE[(X - \mu_X)^2] = m\sigma_X^2$. Moreover, $\sigma_Y = |m|\sigma_X$. Therefore

$$\rho(X, Y) = \frac{\text{Cov }(X, Y)}{\sigma_X \sigma_Y} = \frac{m\sigma_X^2}{\sigma_X |m| \sigma_X} = \frac{m}{|m|} = 1 \text{ or } -1,$$

depending on whether m is positive or negative.

As an example, consider the random variables Y and Z defined on page 155. The reader can verify that $\rho(Y, Z) = -1$. The equation that relates Y and Z is $Z = -1Y + 3$. The graph of this equation is shown below.

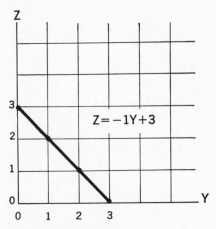

Other Correlated Variables

Suppose X and Y are correlated and $\rho(X, Y)$ is neither 1 nor -1. What does the correlation coefficient (different from 0) signify then? We had an example of such a correlation coefficient before when, using the random variables X and Y defined on page 155, we found that $\rho(X, Y) = .93$. We get a clue to the answer to our question by plotting the pairs of corresponding values of X and Y as points on a graph. These pairs of corresponding values may be read out of the table on page 161. They are (6, 3), (5, 2), (4, 2), (3, 2), (3, 1), (2, 1), (1, 1), and (0, 0). The graph is shown below. Notice that the points do not lie on a straight line, but they *almost do*. Moreover, the line that the points are close to is oblique. A correlation coefficient

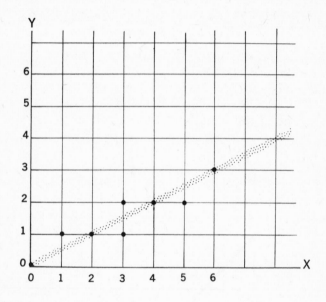

that is not 0, but is neither 1 nor -1 signifies a relationship between two random variables that is *almost linear*. In the customary graph in which pairs of corresponding possible values of the variables are represented by points, the points cluster about some oblique line. The closer the correlation coefficient is to 1 or -1, the closer the points are to the line.

Uncorrelated Variables

To complete our investigation of the meaning of a correlation coefficient, we have to consider the case where $\rho(X, Y) = 0$. In this case we have agreed to say that X and Y are *uncorrelated*. The reader may be tempted to jump to the conclusion that uncorrelated random variables are unrelated random variables in the sense of being independent. However, this conclusion would be wrong. We shall show that while independent random variables are uncorrelated, there are some dependent random variables that are uncorrelated, too.

Suppose X and Y are independent random variables. We shall show that $E(XY) = E(X)E(Y)$. We carry out the details of the proof only for the case where X has only two possible values, x_1, x_2, and Y has only three possible values y_1, y_2, y_3. This will permit us to use the joint probability table that appears on page 163. The method of proof is general, however, and may be used for any two independent random variables. Using the probabilities that appear in the table on page 163, we see that

$$
\begin{aligned}
E(XY) = {} & (x_1y_1)h(x_1, y_1) + (x_1y_2)h(x_1, y_2) \\
& + (x_1y_3)h(x_1, y_3) + (x_2y_1)h(x_2, y_1) \\
& + (x_2y_2)h(x_2, y_2) + (x_2y_3)h(x_2, y_3).
\end{aligned}
$$

The fact that X and Y are independent means that

$$
\begin{aligned}
h(x_1, y_1) &= f(x_1)g(y_1), & h(x_1, y_2) &= f(x_1)g(y_2), \\
h(x_1, y_3) &= f(x_1)g(y_3), & h(x_2, y_1) &= f(x_2)g(y_1), \\
h(x_2, y_2) &= f(x_2)g(y_2), & h(x_2, y_3) &= f(x_2)g(y_3).
\end{aligned}
$$

When we make these substitutions, the expression for $E(XY)$ becomes factorable, and we have

$$
E(XY) = [x_1f(x_1) + x_2f(x_2)][y_1g(y_1) + y_2g(y_2) + y_3g(y_3)].
$$

But the expressions in square brackets are $E(X)$ and $E(Y)$ respectively. So we have $E(XY) = E(X)E(Y)$, when X and Y are independent random variables. It follows from this result immediately that if X and Y are independent random variables, Cov $(X, Y) = 0$. If $\sigma_X \neq 0$ and $\sigma_Y \neq 0$, then $\rho(X, Y) = \dfrac{\text{Cov } (X, Y)}{\sigma_X \sigma_X} = 0$. If either σ_X or σ_Y is 0, then $P(X, Y) = 0$ in any case, by definition. Consequently, *independent random variables are uncorrelated.* The pair of variables, $(U\ V)$, defined on page 155, is an example of variables that are uncorrelated because they are independent.

To show that there are some *dependent* random variables that are uncorrelated, consider the experiment of tossing a fair die twice. Suppose a player *is paid* a number of dollars equal to the number that turns up on the first toss, and he *pays out* a number of dollars equal to the number that turns up on the second toss. Let $X =$ his net gain. We list below the events in the usual 36-element sample space that correspond to each possible value of X. Negative values of X signify a net loss.

Event	x	$P(X = x)$
$\{(1, 6)\}$	-5	$\frac{1}{36}$
$\{(1, 5), (2, 6)\}$	-4	$\frac{2}{36}$
$\{(1, 4), (2, 5), (3, 6)\}$	-3	$\frac{3}{36}$
$\{(1, 3), (2, 4), (3, 5), (4, 6)\}$	-2	$\frac{4}{36}$
$\{(1, 2), (2, 3), (3, 4), (4, 5), (5, 6)\}$	-1	$\frac{5}{36}$
$\{(1, 1), (2, 2), (3, 3), (4, 4), (5, 5), (6, 6)\}$	0	$\frac{6}{36}$
$\{(2, 1), (3, 2), (4, 3), (5, 4), (6, 5)\}$	1	$\frac{5}{36}$
$\{(3, 1), (4, 2), (5, 3), (6, 4)\}$	2	$\frac{4}{36}$
$\{(4, 1), (5, 2), (6, 3)\}$	3	$\frac{3}{36}$
$\{(5, 1), (6, 2)\}$	4	$\frac{2}{36}$
$\{(6, 1)\}$	5	$\frac{1}{36}$

Let $Y = X^2$. The corresponding table for Y is shown below:

Event	y	$P(Y = y)$
$\{(1, 6), (6, 1)\}$	25	$\frac{2}{36}$
$\{(1, 5), (2, 6), (5, 1), (6, 2)\}$	16	$\frac{4}{36}$
$\begin{cases}(1, 4), (2, 5), (3, 6),\\(4, 1), (5, 2), (6, 3)\end{cases}$	9	$\frac{6}{36}$
$\begin{cases}(1, 3), (2, 4), (3, 5), (4, 6),\\(3, 1), (4, 2), (5, 3), (6, 4)\end{cases}$	4	$\frac{8}{36}$
$\begin{cases}(1, 2), (2, 3), (3, 4), (4, 5), (5, 6),\\(2, 1), (3, 2), (4, 3), (5, 4), (6, 5)\end{cases}$	1	$\frac{10}{36}$
$\{(1, 1), (2, 2), (3, 3), (4, 4), (5, 5), (6, 6)\}$	0	$\frac{6}{36}$

The joint probability table for (X, Y) takes this form:

X \ Y	25	16	9	4	1	0	$P(X = x)$
-5	$\frac{1}{36}$	0	0	0	0	0	$\frac{1}{36}$
-4	0	$\frac{2}{36}$	0	0	0	0	$\frac{2}{36}$
-3	0	0	$\frac{3}{36}$	0	0	0	$\frac{3}{36}$
-2	0	0	0	$\frac{4}{36}$	0	0	$\frac{4}{36}$
-1	0	0	0	0	$\frac{5}{36}$	0	$\frac{5}{36}$
0	0	0	0	0	0	$\frac{6}{36}$	$\frac{6}{36}$
1	0	0	0	0	$\frac{5}{36}$	0	$\frac{5}{36}$
2	0	0	0	$\frac{4}{36}$	0	0	$\frac{4}{36}$
3	0	0	$\frac{3}{36}$	0	0	0	$\frac{3}{36}$
4	0	$\frac{2}{36}$	0	0	0	0	$\frac{2}{36}$
5	$\frac{1}{36}$	0	0	0	0	0	$\frac{1}{36}$
$P(Y = y)$	$\frac{2}{36}$	$\frac{4}{36}$	$\frac{6}{36}$	$\frac{8}{36}$	$\frac{10}{36}$	$\frac{6}{36}$	1

It is clear from the table that X and Y are not independent, since the multiplication rule for independent random variables, $P(X = y, Y = y) = P(X = x)P(Y = y)$ is not satisfied.

The reader can verify from these tables that $E(X) = 0$, $E(Y) = \frac{210}{36}$, and $E(XY) = 0$. Consequently Cov $(X, Y) = 0$, and $\rho(X, Y) = 0$. So, in this case, although X and Y are dependent, they are uncorrelated.

Misconceptions About Correlation

There are two common errors about the meaning of correlation. One of them equates the word *uncorrelated* with the word *unrelated*. This error is refuted by the example just given. If X and Y are random variables, and $Y = X^2$, X and Y are certainly related, although they are uncorrelated. The second common error equates *correlation* with *causality*. When $\rho(X, Y)$ has a value that is close to 1 or -1, so that we are justified in saying that the correlation between X and Y is high, it means that fluctuations in X and Y are more or less in step. If ρ is positive, it means that an increase in the value of X is generally accompanied by an increase in the value of Y. If ρ is negative, it means that an increase in the value of X is generally accompanied by a decrease in the value of Y. But it does not mean that the changes in X are necessarily the cause of the changes in Y. Actually there are many different situations that are compatible with a high correlation of X and Y. For example, 1) The changes in X may cause the changes in Y; 2) the changes in Y may cause the changes in X; 3) the changes in X and Y may both be the effects of some other operative cause; 4) the apparent linkage of the fluctuations in X and Y may be purely coincidental. Because of all these different possibilities, a correlation must always be interpreted with caution. A high correlation suggests that some kind of causal relationship may be considered as a possibility, but it does not prove that a causal relationship exists.

The opening sentence of this chapter gives us an example of a correlation that is often misinterpreted. There is a positive correlation between the number of years of schooling an adult has had, and the annual income that he attains. This fact is sometimes cited as proof of the assertion that education increases a person's earning power. However, this fact by itself does not prove the assertion at all. It is possible, for example, that high earning power and high level of education are both consequences of being born into a family with high socio-economic status. It may be true that education increases a person's earning power, but other evidence besides the correlation is needed to prove that it is.

Exercises for Chapter VII

1. From the table on page 155, identify the elements of each of these events, and the probability of the events:

   a) $X = 3$ b) $Y = 2$ c) $(X = 3, Y = 2)$
   d) $Z = 1$ e) $(Y = 2, Z = 1)$ f) $(Y = 3, Z = 3)$
   g) $U = 1$ h) $V = 0$ l) $(U = 1, V = 0)$

   Compare your answers with the corresponding entries in the joint probability tables for (X, Y), (Y, Z), and (U, V) shown on pages 156 and 158.

2. Construct a joint probability table for the pair of random variables (X, Z) defined on page 155. Compute $\rho(X, Z)$.

3. Construct a joint probability table for the pair of random variables (X, U). (See page 155.) Compute $\rho(X, U)$.

4. Supply the missing numbers in the cells of this joint probability table for the pair of random variables (X, Y), assuming that X and Y are independent:

X \ Y	-2	-1	0	1	2	$P(X = x)$
0						$\frac{1}{8}$
1						$\frac{2}{8}$
2						$\frac{3}{8}$
3						$\frac{2}{8}$
$P(Y = y)$	$\frac{1}{10}$	$\frac{2}{10}$	$\frac{1}{10}$	$\frac{3}{10}$	$\frac{3}{10}$	1

5. Using data from the table in exercise 4, prepare tables for the probability functions of the random variables $2X$ and Y^2. Construct the joint probability table for the pair $(2X, Y^2)$, and verify from the table that $2X$ and Y^2 are independent.
6. Verify that U, V, and W, as defined on page 155, are independent random variables.
7. Following a procedure similar to that used on page 168 to derive a formula for Var $(X + Y)$, derive a formula for Var $(X - Y)$. Then show that Var $(X^* - Y^*) = 2(1 - \rho(X, Y))$.
8. If $\rho(X, Y) = -1$, show that possible values of X and Y are related by an equation of the form $Y = mX + b$, where m is negative.
9. Using Y and Z as defined on page 155, show that $\rho(Y, Z) = -1$.
10. Using X as defined below, and $Y = X^2$, construct a joint probability table for (X, Y). Verify that $\rho(X, Y) = 0$. Assume that HH, HT, TH, and TT are equally likely outcomes.

Outcome	HH	HT	TH	TH
x	-2	-1	1	2

11. Examination papers in a certain mathematics class were rated on a scale of 5, the scores 5, 4, 3, 2, 1, 0 corresponding to the letter grades *A*, *B*, *C*, *D*, *E*, *F*. The table below shows *M*, the midterm examination score, and *F*, the final examination score, for each of the 16 students in the class.

Student	*M*	*F*	Student	*M*	*F*
A	2	4	*I*	5	5
B	5	5	*J*	4	5
C	5	5	*K*	5	5
D	3	5	*L*	3	4
E	4	5	*M*	0	1
F	5	2	*N*	3	4
G	5	5	*O*	1	4
H	3	5	*P*	3	2

Construct a joint probability table for the pair of random variables (M, F), and compute $\rho(M, F)$.

CHAPTER VIII

Population Samples

SUPPOSE that, during a national election campaign in the United States, d of the voters favor the Democratic candidate, and r of them favor the Republican candidate. Suppose, too, that this division of sentiment is unknown, and a public opinion poll is undertaken to find out what it is. One way of conducting the poll is to ask *every* voter how he will vote. This method is obviously impractical because it would entail as much work and expense as the national election itself. The practical way is to pick out a sample of the voting population, and ask only those in the sample how they will vote. Two questions come to mind immediately in connection with this shortcut for measuring public opinion. The first question is, how do the poll-takers make sure that they do not bias the result of the poll by a one-sided way of selecting the sample? For example, if the poll is conducted in big cities only, it will be stacked in favor of the Democrats. If the poll is conducted only in rural areas, it will be stacked in favor of the Republicans. To prevent any bias in the poll, the poll-takers must be sure that the sample is selected *at random* from the whole voting population. There are specialized techniques for making random selections from a population. We shall not discuss them any further beyond observing that these techniques exist and have to be used.

The second question is, assuming that the sample is selected at random, what assurance is there that the division of opinion in the sample approximates the division of opinion in the total voting population? This is the question that we shall answer in this chapter.

Population Average and Sample Average

The first step towards answering this question is to reformulate it in a way which permits us to use the concepts developed in preceding chapters. Assign to each Democratic voter the number 1, and to each Republican voter the number 0. In this way, the political preference of the voting population becomes a random variable X with possible values 0 and 1. If the number of Democrats is d and the number of Republicans is r, $P(X = 0) = \dfrac{r}{r + d}$, and $P(X = 1) = \dfrac{d}{r + d}$. Then $E(X) = 0\left(\dfrac{r}{r + d}\right) + 1\left(\dfrac{d}{r + d}\right) = \dfrac{d}{r + d} =$ the fraction of the population that is voting Democratic. So, the information that the poll-takers are trying to find is given by the average value of the random variable X for the whole voting population. Let us call this number the *population average*. Similarly, the division of political opinion in a sample of the population is given by the average value of X for the sample. Let us call this number *the sample average*. The question we are considering may now be reformulated as follows: What assurance is there that the sample average of the values of X is a good approximation to the population average?

To answer this question, we shall take it up in more general form. We shall let X be any random variable over a sample space, which in this context we shall call *the population*. We shall choose at random a sample of size n from this population, and we shall explore the relationship between the sample average and the population average of the values of X. To simplify the problem, we shall assume that the members of the sample are drawn from the population one at a time, *with replacement*. We shall discuss later in this chapter the way in which this assumption affects the accuracy of our conclusions.

A Specific Example

Before we examine the question in general form, we shall explore in detail a specific example. The example will serve a double function. It will give the reader a better grasp of the meaning underlying the symbols that we shall use. It will also help us anticipate the form that the answer to the question will take.

Consider the experiment of tossing two tacks. Assume that for each of them, the probability that the tack falls *point up* is $\frac{3}{4}$, and that the tacks fall independently. Let X = the number of tacks that fall point up. The probability function for X is given by the following table:

x	0	1	2
$P(X = x)$	$\frac{1}{16}$	$\frac{6}{16}$	$\frac{9}{16}$

$E(X) = 0(\frac{1}{16}) + 1(\frac{6}{16}) + 2(\frac{9}{16}) = \frac{3}{2}$. $E(X^2) = 0(\frac{1}{16}) + 1(\frac{6}{16}) + 4(\frac{9}{16}) = \frac{42}{16}$. $\operatorname{Var}(X) = \frac{42}{16} - \frac{9}{4} = \frac{3}{8}$. $\sigma_X = \sqrt{\frac{3}{8}}$. The experiment can be represented by an urn model in which the urn contains chips each of which has on it the number 0, 1, or 2. These numbers occur with the required probabilities if we assume that for every 0-chip in the urn there are 6 1-chips and 9 2-chips. Then tossing the tacks once is like drawing a chip from the urn, and the chips constitute the population that we are investigating. The population average of the variable X is $\frac{3}{2}$.

Now suppose we toss the tacks twice. This is like drawing a sample of two chips from the urn, with replacement after each drawing. Let X_1 be the number on the first chip drawn. Let X_2 be the number on the second chip drawn.

Denote by $\bar{X}$ the average of these two numbers. Then $\bar{X} = (X_1 + X_2)/2$ is the sample average. The sample average is a random variable whose value depends on which two values of X appear on the samples drawn. The table below shows all possible pairs of values of X, the probability of each pair, and the sample average that is obtained from the pair.

Possible values of (X_1, X_2)	Probability of occurrence	$\bar{x}$ (Sample average)
(0, 0)	$\frac{1}{256}$	0
(0, 1)	$\frac{6}{256}$	$\frac{1}{2}$
(0, 2)	$\frac{9}{256}$	1
(1, 0)	$\frac{6}{256}$	$\frac{1}{2}$
(1, 1)	$\frac{36}{256}$	1
(1, 2)	$\frac{54}{256}$	$\frac{3}{2}$
(2, 0)	$\frac{9}{256}$	1
(2, 1)	$\frac{54}{256}$	$\frac{3}{2}$
(2, 2)	$\frac{81}{256}$	2

The probability function for the random variable $\bar{X}$ is shown in this table:

$\bar{x}$	0	$\frac{1}{2}$	1	$\frac{3}{2}$	2
$P(\bar{X} = \bar{x})$	$\frac{1}{256}$	$\frac{12}{256}$	$\frac{54}{256}$	$\frac{108}{256}$	$\frac{81}{256}$

To judge the significance of the sample average $\bar{X}$ in relation to the population average $E(X)$, we first find $E(\bar{X})$, the average value of $\bar{X}$, and determine the extent to which the values of $\bar{X}$ are spread out about its average. The latter information is given by the value of $\sigma_{\bar{X}}$. Computation with the data given above shows that $E(\bar{X}) = \frac{3}{2}$, $E(\bar{X}^2) = \frac{39}{16}$, Var $(\bar{X}) = \frac{3}{16}$, and $\sigma_{\bar{X}} = \sqrt{\frac{3}{16}}$.

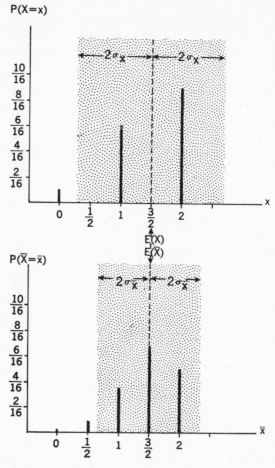

Notice that $E(\bar{X})$ has the same value as $E(X)$. (See the graphs above.) This is significant because $E(\bar{X})$ is the value around which separate values of $\bar{X}$ tend to cluster. Notice, too, that Var $(\bar{X}) = \dfrac{\text{Var } (X)}{2}$ and $\sigma_{\bar{X}} = \dfrac{\sigma_X}{\sqrt{2}}$. This means that the values of $\bar{X}$ do not spread away from the population average as much as the values of X do. Consequently a single value of $\bar{X}$ is more likely to be near $E(\bar{X}) = E(X)$ than a single value of X. That is, the sample average for a sample of size 2 is more likely to be a good estimate of the population average than a single value of X chosen at random.

Any Sample of Any Population

We can now turn to the general problem. Let X be a random variable defined for a particular population. Draw a sample of size n from the population, one member at a time, with replacement of each member drawn before the next one is drawn. Let $X_1, X_2, \ldots, X_n$ be the values of the variable X for the members of the sample. They are random variables, too, since these values may vary from sample to sample. Let $\bar{X} = \dfrac{X_1 + X_2 + \ldots + X_n}{n} = $ the sample average. We shall determine the values of $E(\bar{X})$, Var $(\bar{X})$, and $\sigma_{\bar{X}}$. We note first that the variables X_1, $X_2, \ldots, X_n$ are all identical with the variable X, since they have the same possible values with the same probabilities. Consequently $E(X_1) = E(X_2) = \ldots = E(X_n) = E(X)$, and Var $(X_1) = $ Var $(X_2) = \ldots$ Var $(X_n) = $ Var (X).

The variable $\bar{X}$ can be written in the form $\bar{X} = \dfrac{1}{n} X_1 + \dfrac{1}{n} X_2 + \ldots + \dfrac{1}{n} X_n$. Then, by equation (2) of page 165,

$$E(\bar{X}) = \left(\frac{1}{n}\right) E(X_1) + \left(\frac{1}{n}\right) E(X_2) + \ldots + \left(\frac{1}{n}\right) E(X_n) =$$

$$\left(\frac{1}{n}\right) E(X) + \left(\frac{1}{n}\right) E(X) + \ldots + \left(\frac{1}{n}\right) E(X) =$$

$$n \left(\frac{1}{n}\right) E(X) = E(X).$$ That is, *the average value of all pos-*

sible sample averages for samples of size n is the same as the population average.

Spread of the Sample Average

Before we can compute Var $(\bar{X})$, we need a rule to guide us. We derive this rule first. The experiment of drawing a sample of size n from a population, with replacement, is a compound experiment made up of n identical trials, where each trial consists of drawing one member from the population. They are identical since, after each drawing, the member drawn is replaced, so that successive drawings take place under the same conditions. The conditions of our problem require that the n drawings be independent. The value of X_1 depends only on the first trial, the value of X_2 depends only on the second trial, and so on. Consequently, $X_1, X_2, \ldots, X_n$ are independent random variables. We shall derive a rule for the variance of a sum of n independent random variables, where $n \geqq 2$.

We consider first the sum of two such variables. According to equation (8) on page 169, Var $(X + Y) =$ Var (X) + Var (Y) + 2 Cov (X, Y). When X and Y are independent, Cov $(X, Y) = 0$, and the equation reduces to this form: Var $(X + Y) =$ Var (X) + Var (Y). By a step by step procedure like that used on page 164 to establish equation (1), we can extend this result to more than two independent random variables:

Var $(X_1 + X_2 + \ldots + X_n)$
$$= \text{Var}(X_1) + \text{Var}(X_2) + \ldots + \text{Var}(X_n).$$

On page 148 we saw that Var $(aX) = a^2$ Var (X). Combining these two results, we have

Var $(a_1X_1 + a_2X_2 + \ldots + a_nX_n)$
$$= \text{Var}(a_1X_1) + \text{Var}(a_2X_2) + \ldots + \text{Var}(a_nX_n)$$
$$= a_1^2 \text{Var}(X_1) + a_2^2 \text{Var}(X_2) + \ldots + a_n^2 \text{Var}(X_n),$$

if $X_1, X_2, \ldots X_n$ are independent. In the case under consideration, where $X_1 = X_2 = \ldots X_n = X$, we have

$$\text{Var}\,(\bar{X}) = \text{Var}\left[\left(\frac{1}{n}\right)X_1 + \left(\frac{1}{n}\right)X_2 + \ldots + \left(\frac{1}{n}\right)X_n\right]$$

$$= \frac{1}{n^2}\,\text{Var}\,(X_1) + \frac{1}{n^2}\,\text{Var}\,(X_2) + \ldots + \frac{1}{n^2}\,\text{Var}\,(X_n)$$

$$= n\left(\frac{1}{n^2}\right)\text{Var}\,(X) = \frac{\text{Var}\,(X)}{n}.$$

Consequently $\sigma_{\bar{X}} = \sqrt{\text{Var}\,(X)/n} = \sigma_X/\sqrt{n}$. This means that the larger the size of the sample is, the less the possible sample averages spread around $E(X)$, and the more likely they are to be close to $E(X)$.

To formulate the last statement more sharply, let us suppose that we decide in advance that we want to measure $E(X)$ with a possible maximum error of e. What is the probability that the sample average, $\bar{X}$, will differ from $E(X)$ by at most e? To answer this question with the help of Chebyshev's Inequality, we first express e as a multiple of σ_X.

$$e = \frac{e}{\sigma_{\bar{X}}}\,\sigma_{\bar{X}}$$

Chebyshev's Inequality tells us that

$$P(|\bar{X} - \mu_{\bar{X}}| \leq m\sigma_{\bar{X}}) \geq 1 - \frac{1}{m^2}.$$

Using $\mu_{\bar{X}} = E(X)$, and $m = e/\sigma_{\bar{X}}$, we get

$$P(|\bar{X} - E(X)| \leq e) \geq 1 - \frac{1}{(e/\sigma_{\bar{X}})^2}.$$

Taking into account the fact that $\sigma_{\bar{X}} = \sigma_X/\sqrt{n}$, this inequality becomes,

$$P(|\bar{X} - E(X)| \leq e) \geq 1 - \frac{(\sigma_X)^2}{e^2 n}$$

If we allow n to increase without limit, $(\sigma_X)^2/e^2n$ approaches 0 as a limit. This means that if n is taken large enough, the probability that $\bar{X}$ differs from $E(X)$ by at most e is almost 1. The number e can be chosen arbitrarily as any positive number, no matter how small. So, with probability almost equal to 1, we can get $\bar{X}$ to be as close as we please to $E(X)$ if we take n to be large enough. In other words, *when a sample is large enough, the sample average is almost certain to be a good approximation of the population average*. This is known as the *law of large numbers*. It is the theoretical foundation for all sampling surveys.

Sampling Without Replacement

There is one gap in the argument that remains to be filled. The law of large numbers derived above applies to samples that are drawn with replacement. However, in the usual type of sampling survey, such as a straw vote, or the testing of samples of a machine's output, the samples are withdrawn from the population without replacement. Under these conditions, a somewhat different result is obtained. If N is the size of the population, and n is the size of the sample, we get as before that $E(\bar{X}) = E(X)$. However, Var $(\bar{X})$ is then equal to $\dfrac{\text{Var }(X)}{n}\left(\dfrac{N-n}{N-1}\right)$. The derivation of this formula requires a lengthy computation that we shall omit. The important thing for us to notice is that the factor $\dfrac{N-n}{N-1}$ is almost equal to 1 when N is very large, and n is small compared to N. Then for a very large population, the value of Var $(\bar{X})$ for a sample drawn with replacement is a good approximation to the value of Var $(\bar{X})$ for a sample drawn without replacement. Therefore the results of the last paragraph may be used with confidence in sampling-surveys of large populations.

Long Run Frequencies

When a fair coin is tossed, the probability that it will fall heads is $\frac{1}{2}$. It is common to interpret this statement to mean that if the coin is tossed many times, in the long run about half of the outcomes will be heads. In general, when an experiment is performed, if the probability of an event is p, we interpret this to mean that if the event occurs m times out of n independent trials, then $\frac{m}{n}$ is approximately equal to p, in the long run. We now show that this common interpretation of probability as a long-run relative frequency has a sound foundation in the law of large numbers. Let X be a random variable that has the value 1 when the event in question occurs, and has the value 0 when it does not occur. Then the table for the probability function of X takes this form:

x	0	1
$P(X = x)$	$1 - p$	p

$E(X)$ is easily seen to be equal to p.

Consider as "population" an endless series of trials of the experiment. Then n independent trials constitute a sample of size n drawn from this population. Let X_1, $X_2, \ldots, X_n$ be the values of X that occur. Since the value of each is 0 or 1, if the number 1 occurs m times, then $X_1 + X_2 + \ldots X_n = m$. Then $\bar{X} = m/n$. *The law of large numbers tells us then that if n is large, m/n is almost certainly very close to p.*

Most people refer to this consequence of the law of large numbers as the *law of averages*. Although the law is widely known in this form, it is almost just as widely misunderstood. Suppose a coin is to be tossed 10 times, and the first

7 outcomes are tails. Many people believe that, because of the law of averages, the outcome of the eighth toss is more likely to be heads than tails. This belief is false. In independent tosses of a fair coin, the probability of heads is $\frac{1}{2}$ for every toss. The outcome of earlier trials has no bearing on the outcome of later trials. The law of averages does not say that if there are m heads out of n trials, m/n *must* be approximately equal to $\frac{1}{2}$. It merely says that in many sequences of n tosses, if n is large, values of m/n that are close to $\frac{1}{2}$ are most probable. Values of m/n that are close to 0 or 1 are improbable, but not impossible.

Exercises for Chapter VIII

1. The probability function for a random variable X over a particular population is given by this table:

x	1	2	3
$P(X = x)$	.3	.6	.1

A random sample of size 3 is drawn, with replacement. Let X_1, X_2, X_3 be the values of X for the three elements of the sample respectively. Let $\overline{X}$ be the sample average.

a) Construct a table showing all possible values of (X_1, X_2, X_3), the probability of each triple, and the corresponding value of $\overline{X}$.

b) Compute $E(X)$, $E(\overline{X})$, σ_X, and $\sigma_{\overline{X}}$.

c) Draw a graph for the probability functions of X and $\overline{X}$, using separate axes but the same horizontal and vertical scales for both graphs. To show the spread of each graph, indicate the distance $2\,\sigma_X$ and $2\sigma_{\overline{X}}$ respectively on either side of the mean.

2. If X is a random variable over a given population, and $\overline{X}$ is the sample average for a random sample of size n, drawn

with replacement, for what value of n is $\sigma_{\overline{X}}$ one tenth as large as σ_X?

3. If X is a random variable over a given population, and $\overline{X}$ is the sample average for a random sample of size n. if $\sigma_X = .5$ and $n = 10$, what is the probability that $\overline{X}$ and $E(X)$ differ by at most .5?

4. If X is a random variable over a population of size 1,000, with $\sigma_X = 2$, and $\overline{X}$ is the sample average for a random sample of size 100, compute $\sigma_{\overline{X}}$ a) if the sample is drawn with replacement, and b) if the sample is drawn without replacement. Compare the answers to a) and b).

CHAPTER IX

Trials with Two Outcomes

Success or Failure

THERE are many experiments which have only two possible outcomes. When you toss a coin, the outcome is *heads* or *tails*. When you toss a tack, the tack falls *point up* or *point down*. When a product of a machine is tested, it is examined to see if it is *defective* or *not defective*.

Other experiments may sometimes be thought of as two-outcome experiments, even though the associated sample space has more than two elements. If you are interested only in observing whether a particular event E has or has not occurred, then the two possible outcomes are E and E'. For example, when you roll two dice, E might be the event that the numbers that turn up add up to 7. Then the two possible outcomes are E, with a probability of $\frac{1}{6}$, and E', with a probability of $\frac{5}{6}$. When a two-outcome experiment is studied, it is customary to call one of the events *success* and the other one *failure*. Two-outcome experiments are known as *Bernoulli* experiments, named after the seventeenth century mathematician James Bernoulli. All may be represented by the experiment of tossing a tack, where the possible outcomes have probabilities p and q respectively, and $p + q = 1$.

A compound experiment is said to be made up of *Bernoulli trials* if it is a sequence of independent two-outcome trials in each of which the probability of success has the same value p. Bernoulli trials are studied in great detail because they have many important practical applications.

192

The Number of Successes

Suppose an experiment consists of n Bernoulli trials, in each of which the probability of success is p. Let Y_n be the number of successes that occur in the n trials. Then Y_n is a random variable over the sample space of the experiment. It determines a probability function whose value at r is $P(Y_n = r)$. On page 121 of Chapter V, by studying repeated tossings of a tack, we found this value to be $\binom{n}{r} p^r q^{n-r}$, where $q = 1 - p$ = the probability of failure in one trial. It is customary to represent this number by the symbol $b(r; n, p)$. The entries inside the parentheses in this symbol serve to remind us that while the value of $P(Y_n = r)$ depends on r, it also depends on the value of n and p. The probability function defined by

$$b(r; n, p) = P(Y_n = r) = \binom{n}{r} p^r q^{n-r}$$

is called the *binomial distribution*, because for given p and n the values of $b(r; n, p)$ for $r = 0, 1, \ldots, n$ are the terms of the expansion of $(p + q)^n$ given by the binomial theorem. (See page 79.) Strictly speaking, we have here not just one probability function or distribution but a whole family of functions, because there is a separate one defined for each choice of values of p and n.

Because of their great practical importance, extensive tables for the binomial distribution have been prepared. To show how these tables are used, we reproduce a small section of one of them. There are two types of tables that have been published. One type shows the value of $b(r; n, p)$ for given values of r, n, and p. The other type shows the value of

$$P(Y_n \geq r) = b(r; n, p)$$
$$+ b(r + 1; n, p) + \ldots + b(n; n, p),$$

known as the *cumulative probability* of r or more successes. We use the latter type because it reduces the amount of computation that is needed when the table is used. The value of $b(r; n, p)$ is easily obtained from the cumulative probability table, as we shall see.

In the table reproduced here we have omitted entries for $n = 1$, because these are already known without computation. In one trial, the probability of at least one success = the probability of one success = p. We have also omitted entries for $r = 0$ for all values of n, because these, too, are known without computation. The probability that Y_n is greater than or equal to 0 is the sum of the probabilities of all possible values of Y_n, and therefore is equal to 1.

Several examples, worked out in detail, will show how the table is used.

Take a Number

Among the integers from 1 to 10 inclusive there are four numbers that are prime. So, if a number is chosen at random from the integers from 1 to 10, the probability that it is a prime is .4. Suppose 10 numbers are chosen at random in this way, each choice being made independently from the full set from 1 to 10. What is the probability a) that 5 or more are primes, b) that 4 or more are primes, c) that four of them are primes, d) that three or fewer are primes?

The answer to a) is supplied by the entry in the table for $n = 10$, $p = .4$, and $r = 5$: The probability that at least five of the numbers are prime is .367. The answer to b) is supplied by the entry in the table for the same values of n and p, with $r = 4$: The probability that at least four of the numbers are prime is .618. The answer to c) is given by the difference between the answers to b) and a): .618 − .367 = .251. The event "three or fewer are primes" is the complement of the event "four or more are primes."

So the answer to d) is found by subtracting the answer to b) from 1: $1 - .618 = .382$.

Among the integers from 1 to 10 there are 7 numbers that are not divisible by 3. We say these numbers are *prime to 3*. If 6 numbers are chosen at random, each from the full set of integers from 1 to 10, what is the probability

The Probability of r or More Successes in n Bernoulli Trials

n	r	$p = .01$	$p = .05$	$p = .10$	$p = .20$	$p = .30$	$p = .40$	$p = .50$
2	1	.020	.098	.190	.360	.510	.640	.750
	2		.002	.010	.040	.090	.160	.250
3	1	.030	.143	.271	.488	.657	.784	.875
	2		.007	.028	.104	.216	.352	.500
	3			.001	.008	.027	.064	.125
4	1	.039	.185	.344	.590	.760	.870	.938
	2	.001	.014	.052	.181	.348	.525	.688
	3			.004	.027	.084	.179	.312
	4				.002	.008	.026	.062
5	1	.049	.226	.410	.672	.832	.922	.969
	2	.001	.023	.081	.263	.472	.663	.812
	3		.001	.009	.058	.163	.317	.500
	4				.007	.031	.087	.188
	5					.002	.010	.031
6	1	.059	.265	.469	.738	.882	.953	.984
	2	.001	.033	.114	.345	.580	.767	.891
	3		.002	.016	.099	.256	.456	.656
	4			.001	.017	.070	.179	.344
	5				.002	.011	.041	.109
	6					.001	.004	.016
7	1	.068	.302	.522	.790	.918	.972	.992
	2	.002	.044	.150	.423	.671	.841	.938
	3		.004	.026	.148	.353	.580	.773
	4			.003	.033	.126	.290	.500
	5				.005	.029	.096	.227
	6					.004	.019	.062
	7						.002	.008

Missing values are less than .0005.

The Probability of *r* or More Successes in *n* Bernoulli Trials

n	r	p = .01	p = .05	p = .10	p = .20	p = .30	p = .40	p = .50
8	1	.077	.337	.570	.832	.942	.983	.996
	2	.003	.057	.187	.497	.745	.894	.965
	3		.006	.038	.203	.448	.685	.855
	4			.005	.056	.194	.406	.637
	5				.010	.058	.174	.363
	6				.001	.011	.050	.145
	7					.001	.009	.035
	8						.001	.004
9	1	.086	.370	.613	.866	.960	.990	.998
	2	.003	.071	.225	.564	.804	.929	.980
	3		.008	.053	.262	.537	.768	.910
	4		.001	.008	.086	.270	.517	.746
	5			.001	.020	.099	.267	.500
	6				.003	.025	.099	.254
	7					.004	.025	.090
	8						.004	.020
	9							.002
10	1	.096	.401	.651	.893	.972	.994	.999
	2	.004	.086	.264	.624	.851	.954	.989
	3		.012	.070	.322	.617	.833	.945
	4		.001	.013	.121	.350	.618	.828
	5			.002	.033	.150	.367	.623
	6				.006	.047	.166	.377
	7				.001	.011	.055	.172
	8					.002	.012	.055
	9						.002	.011
	10							.001

Missing values are less than .0005.

that at least 5 of them are prime to 3? In this problem, we have $n = 6$, $p = .7$, and $r = 5$. We cannot read the answer from the table for these values of n, p, and r because there are no entries for $p = .7$. What we have to do in this problem is switch the labels we have attached to the two possible outcomes. Instead of considering the event "prime to 3" as a *success*, consider it as a *failure*. Then, in the notation of the table, $q = .7$, and $p = .3$.

Rephrasing the question in terms of the event that we now consider a *success*, it asks, "What is the probability that at most one number is not prime to 3?" To answer this question, first find the probability that at least two numbers are not prime to 3. For $n = 6$, $p = .3$, and $r = 2$, the table tells us that the probability that at least two numbers are not prime to 3 is .580. Then the probability that at most one number is not prime to 3 is $1 - .580 = .420$. Then the probability that at least 5 of the numbers are prime to 3 is .420.

True or False?

A test consisting of 10 true-false questions was given to a class. Six correct answers were needed to pass the test. One youngster who had not studied for the test chose his answer to each question by tossing a coin. If the coin fell *heads* he wrote *true*. If it fell *tails* he wrote *false*. Under these conditions the probability that any answer was correct is .5. What is the probability that our negligent scholar passes the test? The answer to our question is supplied by the entry in the table for $n = 10$, $p = .50$, $r = 6$. The probability that he passes is .377.

May the Best Man Win

The Ping-pong champions of two schools are competing for a prize. The prize will be awarded to the one who wins a majority of the games in a series of games. One of the players is known to be somewhat better than the other. Suppose the measure of his superiority is expressed in the estimate that in any one game the probability that he will win is .6. What is the probability that the better player will win if the series consists of 3 games? 5 games? 7 games? (Assume that all games in a series are played.) To answer these questions, we first find the probability that the poorer player will win. For a 3-game series, we look up the entry in the table for $n = 3$, $p = .4$, and $r = 2$. For a 5-game series, we use $n = 5$, $p = .4$, and $r = 3$. For a 7-game series, we use $n = 7$, $p = .4$, and $r = 4$. The probabilities that the poorer player wins in a 3, 5, and 7 game series are .352, .317, and .290 respectively. So the probabilities that the better player wins in a 3, 5, and 7 game series are .648, .683, and .710 respectively. The longer the series is, the higher the likelihood is that the better player will win.

Expectation and Standard Deviation

It is useful to know the expectation, or average value, of Y_n for fixed n and p, and its standard deviation. We can compute these numbers, $E(Y_n)$ and σ_{Y_n}, by applying the definitions of expectation and standard deviation. However, there is an easier way, based on the fact that Y_n is the sum of n independent random variables.

For the n Bernoulli trials, define random variables X_1, $X_2, \ldots, X_n$ respectively as follows: For $k = 1, 2, \ldots, n$, $X_k = 1$ if the outcome of the k'th trial is a *success*, and $X_k = 0$ if the outcome of the k'th trial is a *failure*. Then $Y_n = X_1 + X_2 + \ldots + X_n$. Moreover, since each X_k depends only on the k'th trial, $X_1, X_2, \ldots, X_n$ are independent random variables. For each of the random variables X_k, $E(X_k) = 0q + 1p = p$. Applying the formula found on page 164, we have

$$E(Y_n) = E(X_1 + X_2 + \ldots + X_n)$$
$$= E(X_1) + E(X_2) + \ldots + E(X_n)$$
$$= p + p + \ldots + p = np.$$

For each of the random variables X_k, $E(X_k^2) = 0^2q + 1^2p = p$. Var $(X_k^2) = E(X_k^2) - [E(X_k)]^2 = p - p^2 = p(1 - p) = pq$. Applying the formula found on page 186, we have

$$\text{Var } (Y_n) = \text{Var } (X_1 + X_2 + \ldots + X_n)$$
$$= \text{Var } (X_1) + \text{Var } (X_2) + \ldots + \text{Var } (X_n)$$
$$= pq + pq + \ldots + pq = npq.$$

Consequently $\sigma_{Y_n} = \sqrt{npq}$. In the special case of n tosses of a fair coin, $p = q = \frac{1}{2}$, so $E(Y_n) = n/2$, and $\sigma_{Y_n} = \sqrt{n}/2$.

The Probability of Values Close to the Average

In a series of n Bernoulli trials, what is the probability that values of Y_n will be close to the expected value? An approximate answer to this question is given in general terms by the Chebyshev Inequality, which says that the probability that a value differs from the expected value by at most m standard deviations is greater than or equal to $1 - \dfrac{1}{m^2}$. We can make this statement more specific now by using the values of $E(Y_n)$ and σ_{Y_n} obtained in the preceding paragraph. For definiteness, let us take the case where $n = 9$, and $p = .5$. Then $E(Y_9) = \frac{9}{2}$, and $\sigma_{Y_9} = \frac{3}{2}$. Using $m = 2$, the Chebyshev Inequality tells us that the probability that Y_9 differs from $\frac{9}{2}$ by at most 3 is greater than or equal to .75. That is, the probability that Y_9 lies between $\frac{3}{2}$ and $\frac{15}{2}$ inclusive is greater than or equal to .75. Since only integral values of Y_9 are possible, this statement is equivalent to the statement that the probability that Y_9 lies between 2 and 7 inclusive is greater than or equal to .75. We can now check this estimate by using the table on page 196. Using $n = 9$, $p = .5$, and $r = 2$, we find that $P(Y_9 \geqq 2) = .980$. Using $n = 9$, $p = .5$, and $r = 8$, we find that $P(Y_9 \geqq 8) = .020$. Subtracting these figures, we get $P(2 \leqq Y_9 \leqq 7) = .960$. We see that the Chebyshev prediction that this probability is greater than or equal to .750 is a very conservative one indeed.

If we take $m = 1$, the Chebyshev Inequality says that the probability that Y_9 in this case differs from $\frac{9}{2}$ by at most $\frac{3}{2}$ is greater than or equal to 0. This prediction tells us nothing at all, because we already know that *any* probability is greater than or equal to 0. However, we can find the actual probability by consulting the table. Using $n = 9, p = .5$, and $r = 3$, we find that $P(Y_9 \geqq 3) = .910$. Using $n = 9, p = .5$, and $r = 7$, we find that $P(Y_9 \geqq 7) = .090$. Subtracting these figures, we get $P(3 \leqq Y_9 \leqq 6) = .820$. The Chebyshev Inequality is obviously of limited usefulness as an estimate of probabilities when it fails to predict a probability as high as 82%. Of course no estimate is needed when the actual value of a probability can be looked up in a table. However, it is useful to be able to make a reasonable estimate *without using the table*. In the next chapter we shall find another way of making such estimates that is an improvement over the Chebyshev Inequality.

The Incidence of Color-Blindness

In our discussion of Bernoulli trials so far, we have assumed that p, the probability of success, is known, and we have drawn conclusions about the random variable Y_n, the number of successes in n trials. In practice the situation is usually reversed: p is unknown; Y_n is known as the result of an experiment, and we try to draw conclusions about p from the known value of Y_n. For example, let the probability that a person is color-blind be p. To get an estimate of p, we usually examine a large number, n, of people, and count how many of them are color-blind. Since the people examined are selected from a very large population, it is not a serious error to assume that they are drawn from the population with replacement. Then the examination of each person is a Bernoulli trial with probability of success p. In a sample of n people, the number who are color-blind is Y_n, the number of successes in n Bernoulli trials. We take the ratio Y_n/n as an estimate of p. How good an estimate is it? Trying to answer this question is a simple example of a problem in *statistical inference*. We can supply a crude answer now on the basis of the Chebyshev Inequality. We shall get a better answer in the next chapter.

Since Y_n is a random variable, so is Y_n/n. $E(Y_n/n) = \frac{1}{n} E(Y_n) = \frac{1}{n} (np) = p$. This tells us that while different samples of n people may produce different values of Y_n/n, at least the average of all possible values of Y_n/n is equal to the number p that we are trying to estimate. To find out how good an estimate a single value of Y_n/n is, we have to find out the probability that it is close to the average value p. First we compute the standard deviation of Y_n/n. To simplify our notation, let us denote the estimate Y_n/n by e. Then

$$\sigma_e = \frac{1}{n} (\sigma_{Y_n}) = \frac{1}{n} \sqrt{npq} = \sqrt{\frac{pq}{n}}.$$

We know from the Chebyshev Inequality with $m = 2$ that *the probability that e differs from p by at most $2\sigma_e$ is at least 75%*. The value of σ_e depends on the value of p. It can be shown that the largest possible value of σ_e occurs when $p = \frac{1}{2}$. This largest σ_e is therefore equal to $\sqrt{\frac{\frac{1}{2} \times \frac{1}{2}}{n}} = \frac{1}{2} \sqrt{\frac{1}{n}}$. Whenever e differs from p by at most $2\sigma_e$, it also differs from p by at most twice the largest possible value of σ_e. *Consequently the probability is at least 75% that e differs from p by at most $\sqrt{\frac{1}{n}}$.*

If 10,000 people are examined, and we find that 310 of them are color-blind, our estimate e of the incidence of color-blindness is .031. Since $n = 10,000$, $\sqrt{\frac{1}{n}} = .01$. Then the probability is at least 75% that p differs from .031

by at most .01. That is, we are at least 75% sure that p lies between .021 and .041, inclusive.

Testing the Dice

Suppose, when a single die is rolled, we consider the event "5 or 6" to be a *success*. If the die is fair, the probability of success is $\frac{1}{3}$. However, the die may not be fair, in which case the probability of success may be some number $p \neq \frac{1}{3}$. To determine the value of p for one of a certain set of dice, someone once performed the experiment of rolling twelve of these dice 26,306 times. Each roll of the twelve dice was an experiment consisting of 12 Bernoulli trials. For each roll he counted the value of Y_{12}, the number of fives and sixes that turned up. The possible values r of Y_{12} range from 0 to 12. He tabulated the number of times each value occurred in the 26,306 experiments, and then by dividing these numbers by 26,306 he obtained the relative frequency $f(r)$ of each value r. The results of this computation are shown in the second column of the table on page 203.

If the numbers r are thought of as numbers on chips in an urn, with the probability of the occurrence of each number given by $b(r; 12, p)$, then the 26,306 values obtained may be thought of as 26,306 samples withdrawn from the urn with replacement. The population average of Y_{12} is $E(Y_{12}) = 12p$. The sample average is 4.052372, the sum of the numbers $rf(r)$ in the table above. Since, for a large sample, the sample average is probably a good approximation to the population average, we have with high probability the approximate equation, $12p = 4.052372$. Then p, rounded off to four decimal places is probably approximately .3377, which is higher than the value .3333 that it would have if the dice were fair.

What is the value of p for each of these 12 dice? The natural hypothesis to make before the dice are rolled is that they are fair and $p = \frac{1}{3}$. The hypothesis we make

r	$f(r)$	$rf(r)$
0	.007 033	.000 000
1	.043 678	.043 678
2	.124 116	.248 232
3	.208 127	.624 381
4	.232 418	.929 672
5	.197 445	.987 225
6	.116 589	.699 534
7	.050 597	.354 179
8	.015 320	.122 560
9	.003 991	.035 919
10	.000 532	.005 320
11	.000 152	.001 672
12	.000 000	.000 000
		4.052 372

after we have the evidence derived from 26,306 experiments is that $p = .3377$. A way of testing both hypotheses further is to compute $b(r; 12, p)$ for both values of p. This will tell us, for each value of p, the theoretical relative frequency of occurrence of r successes. By comparing these theoretical relative frequencies with the actually observed relative frequencies $f(r)$, we can see which set of figures fits the observed facts best. The values of $b(r; 12, \frac{1}{3})$, $f(r)$, and $b(r; 12, .3377)$ are tabulated below. You can see at a glance that the hypothesis that $p = .3377$ fits the experimental facts better than the hypothesis that the dice are fair.

In practical problems of statistical inference it is often necessary to compare observed frequencies with theoretical frequencies that are predicted on the basis of some hypothesis. A comparison of the two sets of numbers by eye is very crude at best. A more scientific comparison is made by computing from the differences of corresponding

r	$b(r; 12, \frac{1}{3})$	$f(r)$	$b(r; 12, .3377)$
0	.077 707	.007 033	.007 123
1	.046 244	.043 678	.043 584
2	.127 171	.124 116	.122 225
3	.211 952	.208 127	.207 736
4	.238 446	.232 418	.238 324
5	.190 757	.197 445	.194 429
6	.111 275	.116 589	.115 660
7	.047 689	.050 597	.050 549
8	.014 903	.015 320	.016 109
9	.003 312	.003 991	.003 650
10	.000 497	.000 532	.000 558
11	.000 045	.000 152	.000 052
12	.000 002	.000 000	.000 002

observed and theoretical frequencies a number that serves as a measure of the closeness of fit of the two sets of numbers. Then it is possible to find out if the hypothesis is consistent with the observed data by comparing the computed number with the entries in a table known as the *Chi-square* table. This test of closeness of fit is known as the *Chi-square test*. The theoretical justification for it is developed in advanced books on statistical theory.

Quality Control

One of the important uses of the Bernoulli distribution is in quality control of manufactured products. Assume that when a machine produces a product, the probability that the product is defective is p. Then the production of n products by this machine is a sequence of n Bernoulli trials. The probability that r out of n products will be defective is $b(r; n, p)$. Suppose that when the machine is properly adjusted p is no higher than .04. If at any time the manufacturer has reason to suspect that p is higher than .04, he considers the machine out of control. Then he stops the machine to have it adjusted in order to reduce the probability of producing defective products. To find out if the machine is in control or out of control, he selects

n of its products at random and tests them for defects. If the number of defective products r exceeds some fixed number r_0, he concludes that the machine is out of control. If r does not exceed r_0, he concludes that the machine is in control. What values of n and r_0 should he use in applying this test? Part of the answer is given by data taken from the tables of values of $b(r; n, p)$. For any fixed value of p, such as .03, .04, .05, .06, etc., and for a given fixed value of n, the tables will show the probability that r will exceed r_0. The manufacturer will choose values of n and r_0 that will make this probability low when p is less than or equal to .04, and will make it high when p is greater than .04. Then judgments made on the basis of the test will have a high probability of being true. In general, the larger the sample that is tested, the more reliable the judgment will be. However, testing a product often means destroying it. So, for reasons of cost, the size of the sample tested must be kept down. The manufacturer aims to choose values of n and r_0 that provide the most reliable test that is consistent with economy. Ways of making this choice are explained in textbooks on statistics.

Random Walks

In the study of diffusion processes in physics, a problem arises known as the *random walk* problem. It turns out to be an old gambling problem in disguise, and both are intimately related to the Bernoulli distribution.

Suppose a particle moves on a line in accordance with the following rules: it moves once every second, and each move is either one unit to the right or one unit to the left, with equal probability. Then the motion of the particle is called a symmetric random walk in one dimension. Each move is a Bernoulli trial, with probability $p = \frac{1}{2}$ that the particle will move to the right. Suppose the walk goes on for a certain length of time. One of the interesting questions that arises is, "For what fraction of the time is the particle likely to be to the right of its starting point?" Because of the symmetry of the walk, our intuition suggests that there is a high probability that it spends half of the time to the right of its starting point and half of the time to the left of it. But this is another case where our intuition is wrong. It turns out that the particle is most likely to spend nearly all of the time on one side or the other. It is least likely to divide its time equally between the two sides. For example, in a walk that lasts 20 seconds, if at the end of the 20 seconds the particle is found to be to the right of its starting point, the probability that it spent at most 1 second to the left of the starting point is .5379. On the other hand, the probability that it spent 10 seconds on the left and 10 seconds on the right is .0606.

Suppose a gambler tosses a fair coin repeatedly, and wins a dollar every time it falls heads, but loses a dollar every time it falls tails. A gain of a dollar is like one step to the right, and a loss of a dollar is like one step to the left. So the fluctuations in the net gain of the player are precisely the fluctuations of the distance of a particle from the origin when it indulges in a symmetric random walk in one dimension. The fact that the particle is likely to spend much time on one side or the other is equivalent to the fact that either the gambler or his opponent is likely to be in the lead for long stretches of time. In fact, it is not unusual for the winner in such a game to be in the lead nearly all of the time. This fact is emphasized most dramatically by the example cited by the probabilist William Feller in the book listed in the bibliography: If the coin is tossed once a second for 365 days, there is 1 chance in 20 that the winner will be in the lead for more than 364 days and 10 hours.

A symmetric random walk occurs in two dimensions when, at each move, the particle moves one unit left or right or forward or back with equal probability. A symmetric random walk occurs in three dimensions when, at each move, the particle moves left or right or forward or

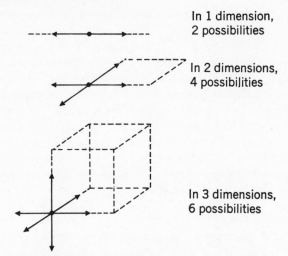

In 1 dimension,
2 possibilities

In 2 dimensions,
4 possibilities

In 3 dimensions,
6 possibilities

Possible moves in a symmetric random walk

back or up or down with equal probability. One of the interesting questions asked about these walks is, "What is the probability that the particle will sooner or later return to its starting point?" For the random walk in one and two dimensions the answer turns out to be 1. Paradoxically, in three dimensions, the probability of a return to the starting point is only about .35.

The Gambler's Ruin

The problem of *the gambler's ruin* arises out of the gambling version of the symmetric random walk in one dimension. Suppose one of the gamblers in the coin tossing game has a capital of *c* dollars when the game begins, and he plays until either he loses all *c* dollars and is ruined, or raises his capital to the amount *d* dollars. Two questions are asked about this game: 1) What is the probability that the gambler is ruined? 2) What is the expected duration of the game? We shall work out the answers to both questions in full.

Let p_c be the probability of the gambler's ruin when his capital is c dollars. We assume that c is greater than 0 but less than d. When the coin is tossed the first time, there are two possible outcomes, each with probability $\frac{1}{2}$. Either he gains a dollar, and his capital becomes $c + 1$, or he loses a dollar, and his capital becomes $c - 1$. The probability of ruin when his capital is $c + 1$ is p_{c+1}. The probability of ruin when his capital is $c - 1$ is p_{c-1}. So the probability of ruin when his capital is c is $p_c = (\frac{1}{2})p_{c+1} + (\frac{1}{2})p_{c-1}$. Solving this equation for p_{c+1}, we get

$$(1) \qquad p_{c+1} = 2p_c - p_{c-1}.$$

To give a meaning to this equation for all values of the subscripts that may arise, we must specify the values of p_0 and p_d. Whenever the gambler's capital is reduced to 0, he is surely ruined. So $p_0 = 1$. On the other hand, if the gambler's capital becomes d, the game ends and he is surely not ruined. So $p_d = 0$. If we list the possible values of c in this problem, they are $0, 1, 2, \ldots, d$, since the game ends when c becomes as low as 0 or as high as d. Corresponding to this sequence of values of c we have the sequence of probabilities of ruin, $p_0, p_1, p_2, \ldots, p_d$. Equation (1) expresses each of the later probabilities in this sequence in terms of the two that immediately precede it. This suggests that we start with the first two, p_0, and p_1, and express all the rest in terms of them. Applying equation (1) with $c = 1$, we get $p_2 = 2p_1 - 1$. So we have a formula that expresses p_2 in terms of p_1. Now use equation (1) with $c = 2$. We get $p_3 = 2p_2 - p_1$. Substituting $2p_1 - 1$ for p_2, we get $p_3 = 3p_1 - 2$. So we now have a formula that expresses p_3 in terms of p_1. Using equation (1) with $c = 3$, we get $p_4 = 2p_3 - p_2$. Substituting $3p_1 - 2$ for p_3, and $2p_1 - 1$ for p_2, we get $p_4 = 4p_1 - 3$. Examination of the formulas for p_2, p_3, and p_4 shows that they follow a pattern. The pattern is given by the general formula $p_c =$

$cp_1 - (c - 1)$. This formula will give us our answer once we know the value of p_1. We find the value of p_1 by letting c take on its highest value d. Then, since $p_d = 0$, we have $dp_1 - (d - 1) = 0$. Solving this equation for p_1, we find that $p_1 = 1 - \dfrac{1}{d}$. Substituting this value of p_1 into the formula for p_c, we get the final answer: $p_c = 1 - \dfrac{c}{d}$. If the gambler's initial capital is \$100, and he plays until he is either ruined or has raised his capital to \$500, then the probability of his ruin is $p_{100} = 1 - \dfrac{100}{500} = .8$.

We follow a similar procedure to find the expected duration of the game. Let N_c be the expected number of tosses of the coin in the entire game when the gambler's capital is c dollars. After the first toss, one toss has already been made. The expected number of tosses after that is $(\frac{1}{2})N_{c+1} + (\frac{1}{2})N_{c-1}$, the average of the expected duration associated with each of the two possible outcomes of the first toss. Consequently, $N_c = 1 + (\frac{1}{2})N_{c+1} + (\frac{1}{2})N_{c-1}$. Solving this equation for N_{c+1}, we get

$$(2) \qquad N_{c+1} = 2N_c - N_{c-1} - 2.$$

When the gambler's capital is reduced to 0 or raised to d the game ends. Consequently $N_0 = 0$, and $N_d = 0$. As in the preceding paragraph, we list the possible values of c in order: $0, 1, 2, \ldots, d$. Corresponding to this sequence of values of c we have the sequence of expected durations of the game, $N_0, N_1, N_2, \ldots, N_d$. Equation (2) expresses each of the later numbers in this sequence in terms of the two that immediately precede it. So, once again, we start with the first two, and through repeated use of equation (2) we derive formulas for the others. Using equation (2) with $c = 1$, and remembering that $N_0 = 0$, we get $N_2 = 2N_1 - 2$. Using equation (2) with $c = 2$, and substituting $2N_1 - 2$ for N_2, we get $N_3 = 3N_1 - 6$. Continuing in this way, we get $N_4 = 4N_1 - 12$, $N_5 = 5N_1 - 20$, and so on. Now we want to determine the pattern followed by these equations that express N_2, N_3, N_4 and N_5 in terms of N_1. We see immediately that the formula for N_c will have the form $N_c = cN_1 - b$. To express b in terms of c, observe that when $c = 2$, $b = 2 = 2^2 - 2$. When $c = 3$, $b = 6 = 3^2 - 3$. When $c = 4$, $b = 12 = 4^2 - 4$. When $c = 5$, $b = 20 = 5^2 - 5$. In general, $b = c^2 - c$, and $N_c = cN_1 - (c^2 - c)$. To find the value of N_1, we make use of the fact that $N_d = 0$. Then $dN_1 - (d^2 - d) = 0$. Solving this equation for N_1, we get $N_1 = d - 1$. Substituting this value of N_1 into the formula for N_c, we get the final formula for the expected duration of the game: $N_c = c(d - c)$. In the case where the gambler starts with a capital of \$100, and plays until he is either ruined or has raised his capital to \$500, the number of tosses in the expected duration of the game is $N_{100} = 100(500 - 100) = 40{,}000$.

There is a physical counterpart to the problem of the gambler's ruin. Let a particle begin a symmetric random walk in one dimension. Place an absorbing barrier c units to the left of the starting point. Place another absorbing barrier d units to the right of this one. Then the walk continues until the particle strikes either barrier and is absorbed. The number $p_c = 1 - \dfrac{c}{d}$ is the probability that it will be absorbed by the barrier on the left. The number

Physical model for the gambler's ruin problem

$N_c = c(d - c)$ is the expected number of steps it will take before it is absorbed by either barrier.

Exercises for Chapter IX

1. Suppose that 5% of the output of a machine is defective. From a batch of several thousand products of the machine, 10 samples are chosen at random. What is the probability that a) at least 1 of the 10 is defective? b) at least 2 of the 10 are defective? c) exactly 1 of the 10 is defective? (Use the table on page 196.)
2. The pupils of a large school were inoculated against polio during 5 consecutive days from Monday through Friday. One fifth of the school was inoculated on each day. If 9 pupils of the school are chosen at random, what is the probability that at most 2 of them were inoculated on Monday?
3. If the better of two baseball teams has a 70% chance of winning any one game against the other, what is the probability that it will win at least 4 games out of 7?
4. If the probability of success in one Bernoulli trial is $\frac{1}{3}$, and Y_{300} is the number of successes in 300 independent trials, find the expectation and standard deviation of Y_{300}.
5. In 9 Bernoulli trials with the probability of success equal to .2, find from the table on page 196 the probability that the number of successes differs from the expected number of successes by at most one standard deviation.
6. A doctor in a large hospital bet $1 even money on every birth in the hospital that the child would be male. He started with a capital of $10, and planned to continue betting until he either lost the $10 or raised his capital to $100. What is the probability that he loses the $10? What is the expected number of bets that he will make? (Assume that male and female births are equally likely.)

CHAPTER X

The Normal Distribution

Representing Probability by an Area

IN THE experiment of tossing six fair coins independently, let X be the number of coins that turn up *heads*. For each integral value of x from 0 to 6, $P(X = x) = b(x; 6, .5)$, and this can be calculated from the table on page 195 by using the column for $p = .5$, and the section of the table for $n = 6$, and subtracting the entry for $r = x + 1$ from the entry for $r = x$. The values of $P(X = x)$ obtained in this way are tabulated below.

x	0	1	2	3	4	5	6
$P(X = x)$	.016	.093	.235	.312	.235	.093	.016

The graph of the probability distribution determined by the random variable X is shown below. For each possi-

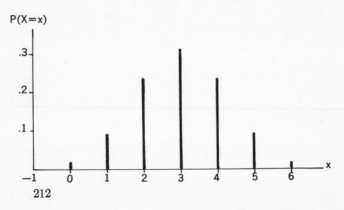

ble value of x, $P(X = x)$ is represented in the graph by the height of a vertical bar. For values of x not in the set $\{0, 1, 2, 3, 4, 5, 6\}$, $P(X = x) = 0$.

We may now disregard the sample space associated with the experiment of tossing six coins, and think of the set of points on the x axis as a sample space, with the probability for each simple event $\{x\}$ in this sample space defined as $P(X = x)$. This new sample space contains an infinite number of simple events, but only a finite number of them have probabilities different from zero. Because of this fact, it has properties very much like those of a finite sample space. In particular, it has the property that the probability of an event E in it is the sum of the probabilities of the simple events that are united in E.

Let E be the event which consists of all the points on the x axis from 1.5 to 2.5 inclusive. Since the only one of these points whose probability is not 0 is the point 2, $P(E) = P(X = 2) = .235$. To show the probability of this event, and to show its association with the event, we draw a rectangle whose base is the event E, namely, the interval from 1.5 to 2.5 inclusive, and whose height is .235 unit. Since the length of the base of the rectangle is 1 unit, the area of the rectangle is .235 square units. Consequently the area of the rectangle represents the probability that X has a value in the interval from 1.5 to 2.5. In the same way, for each value of x in the set $\{0, 1, 2, 3, 4, 5, 6\}$ we can represent the probability that X lies in a unit interval that has x as midpoint by a rectangle whose base is the interval and whose height is $P(X = x)$. The new graph obtained in this way is on page 214. The dark black line is a step-shaped curve that serves in effect as the roof of these probabilities. The probability of each of the seven unit intervals centered at 0, 1, 2, 3, 4, 5, or 6 may be described in terms of this curve as follows: the probability of the interval, (that is, the probability that X lies in the interval), is the area above the interval and between the curve and the x axis. This new way of de-

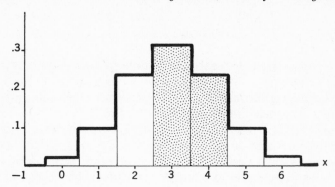

scribing the probability may be extended to some other intervals as well. If a is an integer plus $\frac{1}{2}$, and b is an integer plus $\frac{1}{2}$, then the probability of the interval between a and b is the area above the interval and between the curve and the x-axis. For example, the probability that X lies between $2\frac{1}{2}$ and $4\frac{1}{2}$ is the shaded area in the graph.

Continuous Random Variables

The random variable described above has only a finite number of possible values, 0, 1, 2, 3, 4, 5, and 6. These are represented by *isolated* points on the x-axis. For this reason this random variable is called a *discrete* random variable. There are some practical situations in which a random variable may take on an infinite number of possible values spread out in an entire interval on the x-axis, or even spread out along the entire x-axis. Such random variables are called *continuous*. For example, the time of birth of children born in one day in the United States is a continuous random variable. Children are not born only on the hour. They may be born at any time during the day. If we represent the beginning of the day by 0 and the successive hours of the day by the 24 unit intervals between 0 and 24, then the possible values of the time of birth fill out the whole interval from 0 to 24.

Let us assume that all times of the day are equally likely to be the time of birth of a child. Let us construct a probability model that will show the probability of the values of this continuous random variable. Let us use the set of possible values, the real numbers between 0 and 24, as the sample space. In the case of a finite sample space, we assigned probabilities first to simple events, and then assigned probabilities to events that are not simple by the addition rule of page 36. In this case we shall find it more convenient to work backwards. We shall first assign probabilities to some events that are not simple. Then we shall assign probabilities to the simple events. First consider the event that a birth takes place anytime during the day. This event is represented by the entire interval from 0 to 24. Since all births take place during this interval, its probability is 1. Now consider a four hour interval like the one from 0 to 4. This is only one-sixth of the day. On the assumption that all times of birth are equally likely, the probability that a birth takes place in this interval is $\frac{1}{6}$. In general, if an interval has length n hours, the probability that a birth takes place in that interval is $n/24$. Thus, the probability that a birth takes place between 2 A.M. and 2:30 A.M. is $\frac{1}{48}$. What is the probability that a birth takes place at a particular instant, such as 2 A.M.? To answer this question, we first take an interval which contains the point, and then let the interval shrink in length until it contains only that single point. It will contain the single point only when its length has shrunk to 0 hours. Then the probability that a birth takes place at that instant is $\frac{0}{24}$, or 0. We are thus led to this peculiar result: In a probability model for a continuous random variable X, $P(X = x)$ is 0 for all possible values of X. Now we see why we had to assign probabilities first to intervals rather than to simple events consisting of single points. What we have observed in this case is a characteristic feature of the probability distributions of a continuous random variable: the probability that a single value will occur is 0. However, the probability that the value of the random variable will lie in an interval of length greater than zero may be positive.

Once we have assigned probabilities to intervals, it is a simple matter to assign a probability to a set that is made up of a finite number of non-overlapping intervals: simply add the probabilities of these intervals. For example, if the probability that a child is born between 2 A.M. and 2:30 A.M. is $\frac{1}{48}$, and the probability that a child is born between 5 A.M. and 6 A.M. is $\frac{1}{24}$, then the probability that a child is born between 2 A.M. and 2:30 A.M. or between 5 A.M. and 6 A.M. is $\frac{3}{48}$.

To draw a graph for the probability function of a continuous random variable, we take a hint from the opening section of this chapter. We draw an appropriate curve above the x-axis, so that the probability of an interval on the x-axis may be represented by the area above the interval and between the curve and the x-axis. In the case of the discrete random variable discussed in the opening section, we used such an area to represent the probability of an interval only if each end of the interval was an integer plus $\frac{1}{2}$. In the case of a continuous random variable we impose no such restriction. We use such an area to represent the probability of *any* interval on the x-axis.

It is possible to define the *expectation* and the *standard deviation* of many continuous random variables in a manner analogous to that used for a discrete random variable. The definition employs concepts of the calculus, so we shall not discuss it further.

The Normal Curve

The rest of this chapter is devoted to one particular continuous random variable of great importance. It is known as the *standard normal random variable*. The probability distribution for this variable is called the *normal distribution*. It is represented graphically with the help of a curve known as the *standard normal curve*. The equation of the standard normal curve is

$$y = \frac{e^{-x^2/2}}{\sqrt{2\pi}}.$$

The curve is bell-shaped and is shown on page 218. The probability that the standard normal variable has a value in an interval on the x-axis is the area above that interval and between the curve and the x-axis.

When $x = 0$, $y = e^0/\sqrt{2\pi} = 1/\sqrt{2\pi} = .3989$ approximately, or almost .4. When $x = 4$ or -4, $y = e^{-8}/\sqrt{2\pi} = .0001$ approximately, or almost 0. Although part of the area under the curve lies to the left of $x = -4$ and to the right of $x = 4$, this part is so small that it is negligible. So, for practical purposes, we may assume that all the area under the curve lies over the interval on the x-axis between -4 and 4. This total area is 1. The expectation of the standard normal variable is 0, and its standard deviation is 1. In fact, this is why it is called *standard*, since these are the characteristic features of a *standardized* random variable. (See page 149.)

If a and b are two numbers between -4 and 4, the area under the curve and above the interval of the x-axis that lies between a and b can be computed by the methods of the calculus. The table on page 219 shows the results of these computations for $a = 0$ and $b = x = a$ number between 0 and 4. The examples worked out below show how the table is used to compute the probability for other intervals. For convenience we shall designate the standard normal variable by N^*.

Examples: 1) To find the probability that N^* lies between -3 and 0, we make use of the fact that the standard normal curve is symmetrical. The area above the interval between -3 and 0 is the same as the area above the interval from 0 to 3. This area is given in the table as .4987. So $P(-3 \leq N^* \leq 0) = .4987$.

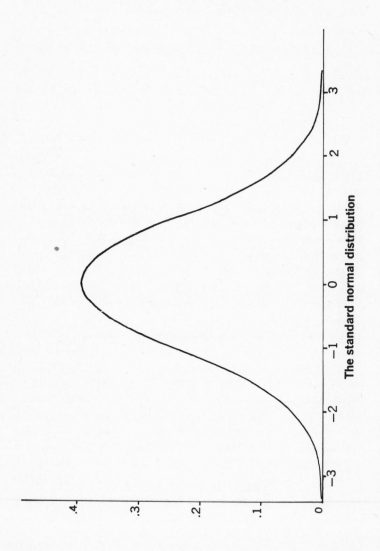

The standard normal distribution

x	$P(0 \leqq N^* \leqq x)$
0.0	.0000
0.1	.0398
0.2	.0793
0.3	.1179
0.4	.1554
0.5	.1915
0.6	.2257
0.7	.2580
0.8	.2881
0.9	.3159
1.0	.3413
1.1	.3643
1.2	.3849
1.3	.4032
1.4	.4192
1.5	.4332
1.6	.4452
1.7	.4554
1.8	.4641
1.9	.4713
2.0	.4772

x	$P(0 \leqq N^* \leqq x)$
2.1	.4821
2.2	.4861
2.3	.4893
2.4	.4918
2.5	.4938
2.6	.4953
2.7	.4965
2.8	.4974
2.9	.4981
3.0	.4987
3.1	.4990
3.2	.4993
3.3	.4995
3.4	.4997
3.5	.4998
3.6	.4998
3.7	.4999
3.8	.4999
3.9	.5000
4.0	.5000

2) To find the probability that N^* lies between -1 and 1, we divide the interval into two disjoint intervals, $-1 \leq N^* < 0$, and $0 \leq N^* \leqq 1$. From the table we find that $P(0 \leqq N^* \leqq 1) = .3413$. $P(-1 \leqq N^* < 0)$ has the same value. So $P(-1 \leqq N^* \leqq 1) = .6826$. Using the same method, we find that $P(-2 \leqq N^* \leqq 2) =$ twice $P(0 \leqq N^* \leqq 2) = 2(.4772) = .9544$.

3) To find $P(1 \leqq N^* \leqq 2)$, we subtract $P(0 \leqq N^* < 1)$ from $P(0 \leqq N^* \leqq 2)$. Then $P(1 \leqq N^* \leqq 2) = .4772 - .3413 = .1359$.

The Central Limit Theorem

The normal distribution is important partly because of its relationship to the binomial distribution. To see the relationship between two distributions, we may compare their graphs in which probabilities are represented by areas under a curve. But first the two graphs must be made comparable by putting them in the same place and drawing them to the same scale. This is accomplished by standardizing the random variables whose probability distributions are being compared. When both variables are standardized, their expectations are both 0, and their standard deviations are both 1. The standard normal random variable is already standardized. So we need only standardize the random variable of the binomial distribution in order to make the comparison. In the preceding chapter we called this random variable Y_n, the number of successes in n Bernoulli trials in each of which the probability of success is p. If μ is the expectation of Y_n, and σ is the standard deviation of Y_n, then the standardized random variable derived from Y_n is $Y_n^* = (Y_n - \mu)/\sigma$.

We shall carry out the comparison in detail for a specific choice of values of n and p. Let $n = 9$, and $p = .20$. Denote the number of successes in 9 trials by X rather than Y_9 in order to simplify the notation. Using the formulas on page 198, we find that the expectation of X is 1.8, and its standard deviation is 1.2. So to compute values of the standardized random variable, we use the formula $X^* = (X - 1.8)/1.2$. To get an area graph for the probability distribution of X^*, we first obtain the data needed for an area graph for X, using the method employed in the opening section of this chapter. The first step is to use the table on page 196 to compute the values of $P(X = r) = b(r; 9, .20)$. The table of values obtained is shown below. (The values for $r = 7$, 8, and 9 are not shown because they are less than .0005.)

x	0	1	2	3	4	5	6
$P(X = x)$	.134	.302	.302	.176	.066	.017	.003

The second step is to associate each of these computed probabilities not with the point x but with the interval between $x - \frac{1}{2}$ and $x + \frac{1}{2}$. This association is shown in the next table:

Interval	−.5 to .5	.5 to 1.5	1.5 to 2.5	2.5 to 3.5
P (Interval)	.134	.302	.302	.176

Interval	3.5 to 4.5	4.5 to 5.5	5.5 to 6.5
P (Interval)	.066	.017	.003

From this last table we can get the data needed for an area graph for the probability distribution for X^* by merely replacing values of X by corresponding values of X^*. For example, if $X = -.5$, $X^* = (-.5 - 1.8)1.2 = -1.9$. If $X = .5$, $X^* = (.5 - 1.8)/1.2 = -1.1$. The resulting table for the probability distribution of X^* is shown below:

Interval	−1.9 to −1.1	−1.1 to −0.3	−0.3 to 0.6	0.6 to 1.4
P (Interval)	.134	.302	.302	.176

Interval	1.4 to 2.3	2.3 to 3.1	3.1 to 3.9
P (Interval)	.066	.017	.003

The area graph for the probability distribution of X^* is shown in the left-hand diagram, p. 222. In the right-hand diagram, the normal curve has been drawn as well, so that both graphs may be compared. Notice that the step-

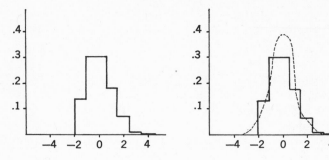

shaped curve of the probability distribution of X^* is an approximation to the normal curve. The significance of this fact is that probabilities of intervals read from one curve are approximately equal to corresponding probabilities read from the other. In this case, the approximation is still a crude one. But if we repeat the same procedure for higher and higher values of n, while keeping p fixed, we find that the approximation becomes better and better. As n approaches infinity, the step-shaped curve of the probability distribution of the standardized random variable of the binomial distribution approaches the normal curve as a limit. This fact is known as the *central limit theorem* of DeMoivre and La Place.

To show the comparison of the two distributions in another way, we tabulate side by side the values of $P(X^* \geq r)$ obtained from the binomial distribution with $n = 9$ and $p = .20$, and the values of $P(N^* \geq r)$. The first set of values is obtained from the table on page 196. The second set of values is computed from the table on page 219. The results are tabulated on page 223. To show how the entries in this table are obtained, let us trace the steps for obtaining those on the third line. The number -0.3 is the value of X^* when $X = 1.5$. So $P(X^* \geq -0.3) = P(X \geq 1.5) = P(X \geq 2)$, which is equal to .564, according to the table on page 223. To obtain $P(N^* \geq -0.3)$, we observe that this is the area under the normal curve above the interval of the x-axis from

r	$P(X^* \geqq r)$	$P(N^* \geqq r)$
−1.9	$P(X^* \geqq -1.9) = P(X \geqq -.5) = 1.000$	.971
−1.1	$P(X^* \geqq -1.1) = P(X \geqq \quad .5) = \quad .866$	.864
−0.3	$P(X^* \geqq -0.3) = P(X \geqq \quad 1.5) = \quad .564$	.618
0.6	$P(X^* \geqq \quad 0.6) = P(X \geqq \quad 2.5) = \quad .262$	.274
1.4	$P(X^* \geqq \quad 1.4) = P(X \geqq \quad 3.5) = \quad .086$	.081
2.3	$P(X^* \geqq \quad 2.3) = P(X \geqq \quad 4.5) = \quad .020$	.011
3.1	$P(X^* \geqq \quad 3.1) = P(X \geqq \quad 5.5) = \quad .003$	.001
3.9	$P(X^* \geqq \quad 3.9) = P(X \geqq \quad 6.5) = \quad .000$	.000

−0.3 to 4. This area is equal to (the area over the interval from −0.3 to 0) + (the area over the interval from 0 to 4) = .1179 + .5000 = .6179 = .618.

Notice that even in this case where n is only 9, the correspondence of the two sets of values is pretty close. The correspondence is even closer for large values of n. *For large values of n, the correspondence is so close that for practical purposes, the normal distribution may be substituted for the standardized binomial distribution.*

Improving on the Chebyshev Inequality

For any random variable X, the Chebysev Inequality gives us an estimate of the probability that values of X lie within a certain distance of $E(X)$. If X is the random variable of a binomial distribution, we get a better estimate by using the central limit theorem.

For example, the Chebyshev Inequality tells us that the probability that values of X lie within a distance of 2 standard deviations from $E(X)$ is at least 75%. This is equivalent to saying that the probability that values of X^* lie between −2 and 2 is at least 75%. If X is the random variable of a binomial distribution for n Bernoulli trials, and n is large, the central limit theorem tells us that the probability that values of X^* lie between -2 and 2 is approximately equal to the probability that values of N^* lie between -2 and 2. This probability was calculated in example 2) on page 219, and was found to be .9544, or about 95%.

The Chebyshev Inequality gives no useful information about the probability that values of X lie within a distance of 1 standard deviation from $E(X)$, because it merely asserts that this probability is greater than 0. But if X is the random variable of a binomial distribution for large n, the central limit theorem tells us that this probability is approximately equal to the probability that values of N^* lie between -1 and 1. The latter probability, also computed in example 2) on page 219, is about 68%.

In Chapter IX we made an estimate of the probability that Y_n/n is a good approximation to p, when Y_n is the number of successes in n Bernoulli trials in each of which the probability of success is p. We found then, by applying the Chebyshev Inequality, that there is a probability of at least 75% that Y_n/n differs from p by at most $\sqrt{1/n}$. This maximum distance, $\sqrt{1/n}$, was the greatest possible value of 2 standard deviations, obtained when $p = \frac{1}{2}$. Now we know from the central limit theorem that if n is large, the probability is not merely at least 75%, but is actually about 95%. If $n = 10,000$, $\sqrt{1/n} = .01$. So, in a sequence of 10,000 Bernoulli trials, the probability is about 95% that the empirical relative frequency of success, Y_n/n, falls within a distance of .01 from p.

Normal Distribution in Nature

A random variable is said to be *normal* if the standardized random variable that corresponds to it is the standard normal variable. We have just seen that the random variable underlying a binomial distribution for n Bernoulli trials is approximately normal if n is large. Another reason why the standard normal distribution is important is that there are many random variables in nature that are approximately normal. Some typical random variables that are approximately normal are these: the height of men of a given age; the number of kernels on an ear of corn of a given variety; the number of ridges on a scallop shell; the I.Q. of children of a given age; the scores by college applicants on the mathematical aptitude test given by the College Entrance Examination Board. In fact, whenever some naturally occurring trait is measured for all members of a population, the measures are found to vary, and the measure, considered as a random variable, is found to be approximately normal.

This fact raises an interesting and important question. Why is the measure of a naturally occurring trait of a population an approximately normal random variable? There is a clue to the answer to this question in an observation we made in Chapter IX. There we found that the random variable Y_n is the sum of n independent random variables, $X_1, \ldots, X_n$, (see page 198), while in this chapter we found out that Y_n is approximately normal. This is an example of a general rule that is proved in advanced texts on probability theory: Under fairly general conditions (which we shall not specify here), if a random variable is the sum of many independent random variables, then it is approximately normal. On the basis of this rule we can understand, for example, why the height of men of a given age is an approximately normal random variable. There are many factors that influence a person's height. Some of them are hereditary. Others are environmental, such as the person's diet, the amount of sleep he gets, etc. It seems reasonable to assume that there is a set of *independent* factors, F_1, F_2, etc., each of which has some bearing on a person's height. The influence of each factor varies from person to person. For example, if F_1 is a particular gene, some people may have it in their heredity, while others do not. Consequently the amount of height contributed by each factor is a random variable. The total amount of height is the sum of the contributions made by all these factors, and hence is the sum of independent random variables. If this surmise is correct, it suffices to explain why height is an approximately normal random variable.

College Board Scores

If a college applicant receives a score of 720 or more on the mathematical aptitude test of the College Entrance Examination Board, where does he stand in comparison with all the applicants of that year? This question is easily answered on the basis of the fact that the score is an approximately normal random variable. Scores on the test are given on a scale that extends from 200 to 800, and the distribution of scores is such that the expectation is 500, and the standard deviation is 100. To answer the question, let X denote the score of any applicant. Then X^*, the corresponding standardized random variable, is given by the formula $X^* = (X - 500)/100$. Then the standardized score that corresponds to $X = 720$ is $X^* = 2.2$. $P(X \geq 720) = P(X^* \geq 2.2) = P(N^* \geq 2.2)$. To compute $P(N^* \leq 2.2)$, we use the table on page 219. There we find that $P(0 \leq N^* \leq 4) = .5000$, while $P(0 \leq N^* \leq 2.2) = .4861$. Subtracting these two numbers, we find that $P(N^* \geq 2.2) = .0139$, or about 1.4%. So an applicant who scores 720 or more is in the top 1.4% of the set of all applicants.

Exercises for Chapter X

1. Use the table on page 219 to find the following probabilities:

   a) $P(-1.5 \leq N^* \leq 0)$;   b) $P(-1.5 \leq N^* \leq 1.5)$;
   c) $P(1.5 \leq N^* \leq 2.5)$.

2. If X is the number of heads that turn up in six independent tosses of a fair coin, find $E(X)$ and σ_X. Then find the value r of X^* that corresponds to each of these values of X: -0.5, 0.5, 1.5, 2.5, 3.5, 4.5, 5.5, and 6.5. Then construct a table like that on page 223 showing the value of $P(X^* \geqq r)$ and $P(N^* \geqq r)$ for each of these values of r.

3. What per cent of all college applicants who take the College Entrance Examination Board mathematics aptitude test get a) a score of 650 or higher? b) a score between 650 and 700? c) a score of 400 or lower? (See page 226.)

CHAPTER XI

Raisins, Stars, and Flying Bombs

Raisin Bread

A RECIPE for raisin bread calls for ingredients in these proportions: 1 cake of yeast, 1 teaspoon of salt, 8 cups of flour, $2\frac{1}{2}$ cups of milk, $\frac{1}{2}$ cup of sugar, 4 tablespoons of butter, and $\frac{1}{4}$ cup of raisins. A bakery uses these proportions to mix a large quantity of dough in order to bake many loaves of bread. The dough is allowed to rise to four times its volume before it is baked. Assuming that each loaf is 7″ long, 4″ wide, and 4″ high, and that the volume of a raisin is approximately .03 cu. in., what is the probability that a loaf of bread contains exactly r raisins, where r is a nonnegative integer? We can answer this question on the assumption that there is thorough mixing of the ingredients so that the raisins are randomly distributed in the dough.

The total volume of the ingredients listed in the recipe is about $11\frac{1}{2}$ cups. Of this volume, only $\frac{1}{4}$ cup consists of raisins. So, when the dough is first mixed, only 1 part out of 46 consists of raisins. After the dough has risen, only 1 part out of 184 consists of raisins. The volume of a loaf of bread is 112 cu. in. The raisins in a loaf may be thought of as occupying cells each of which has a volume of .03 cu. in. Imagine the rest of the loaf divided into cells of the same size. Then the total number of cells is 3,733. Our problem is to determine the probability that r of them are occupied by raisins. The probability that any one cell is occupied by a raisin is $\frac{1}{184}$. Filling the 3,733 cells is like performing an experiment made up of 3,733 Bernoulli trials with $p = \frac{1}{184} = .005$. Then the probability that a loaf of bread contains r raisins is $b(r; 3733, .005)$. The expected number of raisins is $3733(.005) = 18.7$.

To answer the question we used a cell model that can be described more generally as follows: Objects are placed into n cells, with at most one object in each cell. The probability that an object is placed in a cell is p. Whether or not a cell is filled is assumed to be independent of what happens in the other cells. The probability that r cells are filled is $b(r; n, p)$. In this problem concerning raisin bread, the following special conditions are satisfied: 1) n is a large number; 2) p is a small number; 3) their product, np, which we shall denote by λ (lambda), is of moderate size. We shall show that when these three conditions are satisfied, $b(r; n, p)$, which may also be written as $b(r; n, \lambda/n)$, can be replaced by another formula that is easier to use for computational purposes and yields approximately the same values as $b(r; n, p)$ does.

More About e

In the derivation of the new formula we shall have to make use of a property of the number e that was defined on page 85. We first establish this property. It was stated on page 86 that $e^{-1} =$ the limit of $\left(1 - \dfrac{1}{n}\right)^n$ as n approaches infinity. Consequently, if n is large, e^{-1} is approximately equal to $\left(1 - \dfrac{1}{n}\right)^n$. If we use the symbol $\approx$ to mean *is approximately equal to*, then we may write $e^{-1} \approx \left(1 - \dfrac{1}{n}\right)^n$, when n is large. Suppose n/λ is large. Then we may write n/λ in place of n in this formula, and we get

$e^{-1} \approx (1 - \lambda/n)^{n/\lambda}$. Raising both sides of this approximate equality to the λ power, we get $e^{-\lambda} \approx (1 - \lambda/n)^n$. This is the property that we shall have to use in the next paragraph.

An Approximation for $b(r; n, p)$

The new formula will be an approximation for $b(r; n, p)$ when n is large, p is small, and $\lambda = np$ is moderate. We shall derive the formula step by step, by first taking $r = 0$, then $r = 1$, $r = 2$, and so on.

We know that $b(r; n, p) = \binom{n}{r} p^r q^{n-r}$, where $q = 1 - p$. In the case where $r = 0$, $\binom{n}{0} = 1$, $p^0 = 1$, and $q^{n-0} = (1 - p)^n$. So $b(0; n, p) = (1 - p)^n = (1 - \lambda/n)^n \approx e^{-\lambda}$. Using this value of $b(0; n, p)$ as a starting point, we shall get the values of $b(r; n, p)$ for higher values of r by a chain of successive multiplications as follows:

$$b(1; n, p) = b(0; n, p) \times \frac{b(1; n, p)}{b(0; n, p)}.$$

$$b(2; n, p) = b(1; n, p) \times \frac{b(2; n, p)}{b(1; n, p)}.$$

$$\ldots\ldots\ldots\ldots\ldots\ldots\ldots\ldots\ldots\ldots\ldots\ldots$$

$$b(r; n, p) = b(r - 1; n, p) \times \frac{b(r; n, p)}{b(r - 1; n, p)}$$

First we get an approximate value of the ratio used as a multiplier in the last equation above. We make use of the fact that

$$b(r; n, p) = \binom{n}{r} p^r q^{n-r} = \frac{n(n - 1) \ldots (n - r + 1)}{1 \times 2 \times \ldots r} p^r q^{n-r}.$$

Then

$$\frac{b(r; n, p)}{b(r - 1; n, p)} = \frac{n(n - 1) \ldots (n - r + 1)}{1 \times 2 \ldots \times r} p^r q^{n-r}$$

$$\div \left[\frac{n(n - 1) \ldots (n - r)}{1 \times 2 \ldots \times (r - 1)} p^{r-1} q^{n-r+1} \right]$$

$$= \frac{(n - r + 1)p}{rq} = \frac{np - (r - 1)p}{rq}.$$

Now $np = \lambda$. Moreover, since p is small, $q \approx 1$. Also, when r is small compared to n, $np - (r - 1)p \approx np$. Making these substitutions, we get

$$\frac{b(r; n, p)}{b(r - 1; n, p)} \approx \frac{\lambda}{r}.$$

Consequently, the successive multipliers, beginning with $r = 1$, are $\lambda/1$, $\lambda/2$, $\lambda/3$, and so on. Then

$$b(1; n, p) \approx \frac{\lambda}{1} b(0; n, p) \approx \frac{\lambda}{1} e^{-\lambda}.$$

$$b(2; n, p) \approx \frac{\lambda}{2} b(1; n, p) \approx \frac{\lambda \times \lambda}{2 \times 1} e^{-\lambda}.$$

. . . .

$$b(r; n, p) \approx \frac{\lambda}{r} b(r - 1; n, p)$$

$$\approx \frac{\lambda \times \lambda \times \ldots \times \lambda}{r \times (r - 1) \times \ldots \times 1} e^{-\lambda} = \frac{\lambda^r}{r!} e^{-\lambda}.$$

Then the new formula that takes the place of $b(r; n, p)$ or $b(r; n, \lambda/n)$ is $\dfrac{\lambda^r}{r!} e^{-\lambda}$. The latter expression is designated by $p(r; \lambda)$, where it is understood that $\lambda > 0$, and r is a nonnegative integer. The probability distribution that it determines is called the Poisson distribution, after Simeon Poisson (1781–1840). We have derived the Poisson distribution as an approximation to the binomial distribution under special conditions. However, it is important in its own right as a probability function with many important uses.

We can easily verify that $p(r; \lambda)$ qualifies as a probability distribution in its own right. To do so, it merely has to satisfy two conditions required of all probability functions: 1) every value of the function must be positive or 0; 2) the sum of the values of the function for all possible values of r must be 1. The first condition is satisfied because, since λ is positive, λ^r, $r!$, and $e^{-\lambda}$ are all positive. To verify the second condition we observe that

$$p(0; \lambda) + p(1; \lambda) + p(2; \lambda) + \ldots p(r; \lambda) + \ldots$$

$$= e^{-\lambda} + \frac{\lambda}{1!} e^{-\lambda} + \frac{\lambda^2}{2!} e^{-\lambda} + \ldots \frac{\lambda^r}{r!} e^{-\lambda} + \ldots$$

$$= e^{-\lambda} \left(1 + \frac{\lambda}{1!} + \frac{\lambda^2}{2!} + \ldots + \frac{\lambda^r}{r!} + \ldots \right) = e^{-\lambda} \times e^{\lambda} = 1,$$

where the final step makes use of the formula for e^x given on page 86.

Stars, Mice, and Telephone Calls

The formula $p(r; \lambda)$ gives the probability that a loaf of bread contains exactly r raisins, if the raisins are scattered at random in the dough from which the loaf was cut, and λ is the average number of raisins per loaf. Obviously the formula will still apply if we replace the loaf of bread by any unit of space, and the raisins by objects that are scattered at random in space. Moreover, it makes no difference whether the space is three-dimensional, two-dimensional, or one-dimensional, because the same reasoning can be applied in all three cases. In all three cases, the unit of space may be thought of as divided into cells so small that each cell contains either one or none of the scattered objects. Then, as long as the number of cells n

is large, the probability p that an object is placed in one cell is small, and np, the average number of objects per unit of space, is moderate, the argument developed in this chapter will be valid.

Other examples of objects scattered at random in three-dimensional space are: the stars in space; weed seeds in a mass of grass seed. Examples of objects scattered at random in two-dimensional space are: nests of mice in a field; hits by the flying bombs that fell on London in World War II; bacteria colonies growing in a Petri dish. An example of objects scattered at random in one-dimensional space is given by the telephone calls handled by the telephone exchange during the busy hours. The one-dimensional space in this case is the ordered array of instants of time. The occurrence of random telephone calls in time is like the random scattering of points on a line. In all these cases the probability that r of the scattered objects land in a unit of space is given by $p(r; \lambda)$, where λ is the average number of objects per unit of space.

The Poisson distribution, the binomial distribution, and the normal distribution, all related to each other as we have seen, dominate advanced probability theory and its applications.

Exercises for Chapter XI

1. Under the conditions described in the first paragraph of this chapter, the probability that a loaf of raisin bread contains exactly 24 raisins is $b(24; 3735, .005)$, with $\lambda = 18.7$. Then $b(24; 3733, .005) \approx p(24; 18.7) = (18.7)^{24}e^{-18.7}/24!$. Use the tables on page 87 and page 88 to evaluate this expression.
2. For $n = 10$, $p = .1$, $\lambda = np = 1$. Compute the values of $b(2; 10, .1)$ and $p(2; 1)$ to see if they are approximately equal.

CHAPTER XII

Chance in Nature

THE theory of probability was invented to be used in dealing with chance events in nature. Here the word *nature* is used in the broadest possible sense, so that it embraces all phenomena, whether they be physical, biological, or social. In the mathematical theory, the probability of an event is merely a number attached to a subset of a sample space. But when we associate it with some real event in nature, it takes on a new character derived from this association. In this chapter we consider some of the questions that arise when we try to understand the character of applied probability. We shall discuss briefly four questions that have been subjects of much thought and argument: 1) the meaning of probability, in its applications; 2) the relationship between probability and induction; 3) the relationship between chance and causality; 4) the relationship between chance and evolution.

The Meaning of Probability

When a fair coin is tossed, the probability that it will fall heads is $\frac{1}{2}$. The early students of probability all agreed that this statement is true, but they did not agree on what it means. As we stated in Chapter I, two different interpretations of probability arose, the subjective and the physical. In the physical interpretation, the probability of an event is really a property of an endless chain of independent trials for which the event is a possible outcome. For any finite number of trials, we can compute the relative frequency of occurrence of the event by dividing the number of occurrences by the number of trials. In the physical view, the probability is the limit approached by the relative frequency as the number of trials increases to infinity. We have seen that there is some support for this view in the law of large numbers, discussed on page 189.

In the subjective view probability is interpreted as a measure of a person's degree of belief in a statement. The degree of belief is supposed to be based on the completeness of the evidence on which the statement is based. In one extreme version of the subjective view, the absence of any evidence for or against the truth of a statement automatically gives the statement a probability of $\frac{1}{2}$ of being true. This version is now universally rejected. There is a more conservative version of the subjective view in which the probability that a statement is true is really understood to be a property of a class of statements to which this particular statement belongs. For example, if the weatherman says it will rain tomorrow, and we say the probability that his prediction is correct is 85%, we may interpret this to mean that out of 100 predictions of rain by this weatherman, past experience shows that about 85 will prove to be correct, and 15 will prove to be false. This version of the subjective view is essentially the same as the physical interpretation of probability, since the probability of a statement is then the probability of the event that the statement turns out to be true, and is approximated by the long-run frequency with which the event occurs in a series of trials consisting of observations to determine whether the statement is true or false.

Probability and Induction

Some of the early students of probability tried to develop a theory of inductive reasoning on the basis of the subjective view of probability. They argued that while deductive reasoning from true premises can produce conclusions that are *certainly* true, inductive reasoning from observed facts can produce only conclusions that are *probably* true. They cited as an example of this kind of inductive reasoning the argument that since the sun has been known to rise every day for thousands of years it will probably rise tomorrow. Some of the theorists even went so far as to "derive" a formula for the probability that the sun will rise, in terms of the number of times the sun has been observed to rise in the past. The conclusion embodied in the formula was that the greater the number of days that the sun has risen, the more certain it is to rise again for another day. The same kind of reasoning would lead to the conclusion that the greater the number of years that a man has lived, the more certain it is that he will live for another year. This conclusion is obviously not correct.

The attempt to develop a probabilistic theory of induction failed because it was based on a complete misunderstanding of the nature of inductive reasoning in the sciences. Scientists develop general rules (so-called scientific laws) on the basis of particular observed facts. However, they do not squeeze the general rule out of the observed facts the way a cider-press squeezes cider out of apples. Formulation of the rule involves a creative act of the human mind, the creation of a *concept*. In the case of the rising of the sun, the concept, in its modern version, is the Copernican theory of the solar system. The theory is a model which successfully explains *why* the sun rises, and many other seemingly unrelated facts. We are confident that the sun will rise tomorrow, not merely because it has risen before, but because its rising is a necessary consequence of the theory. Induction does not extrapolate from past events to future events by merely extending into the future repetitions that have occurred in the past. Induction extrapolates from the past into the future by creating a conception of a mechanism that explains the past and from which the future can be deduced.

Chance and Causality

Up to the end of the nineteenth century, the scientific laws used by physicists to extrapolate to the future from the past were based on the principle of causality. This principle assumed that the future is bound to the past by the bonds of necessity, so that no effect occurs without a cause, and a given set of causes operating under a given set of circumstances always produces the same effects. During the twentieth century this principle ran into trouble when physicists investigated the behavior of particles within the atom. There is a superficial resemblance between an atom and the solar system. Electrons revolve around the nucleus of an atom, just as the planets revolve around the sun. But while our Copernican model of the solar system permits us to predict where a planet will be at any moment, no existing model of an atom can predict where an electron will be at any moment. The quantum-mechanical models of the atom merely assign to each possible position of an electron the probability that it is there. Moreover, it seems to be inevitable that we cannot pinpoint the position of an electron, because the mere act of observing it with a beam of light kicks the electron and introduces some indeterminacy in its position. Some physicists have concluded that this means that the behavior of electrons is not governed by causality, but is a manifestation of the operation of pure chance. Other physicists, notably Albert Einstein, never accepted this conclusion. Recently, under the leadership of De Broglie and Bohm, attempts have been made to re-assess the role of chance and causality in physical phenomena. The view of Bohm, expressed in his book, *Causality and Chance in Modern Physics*, is that both chance and causality play a part in every physical system observed by man. A scientist never observes the entire universe. He always observes only a part of it. He marks out an area of observation that serves as the context of his studies. The causal laws that he formulates are based on observations within this context and are valid only in this context. However, influences that originate outside this context do intrude their effects into it. These effects appear as chance occurrences, not attached to any known cause, since their causes lie outside the context of the investigation. However, if the context is widened sufficiently, these outside influences may become inside influences, and causal laws governing their behavior may be discovered. But then new chance occurrences will become evident, injected by influences that originate outside the widened context. From this point of view, the description of physical reality in any context always requires two types of laws, causal laws, and laws of chance. The essential feature of a causal law is that it can make predictions about each individual object in the domain for which the law is relevant. For example, Newton's theory of gravitation makes predictions about the motion of each massive body in the solar system. The essential feature of a law of chance is that, while it makes no predictions about individual objects in the domain for which it is relevant, it does make predictions about groups of such objects. The laws of chance are assertions about statistical aggregates. They uncover the constant residue in the behavior of a group when the chance variations of the individuals in the group cancel each other out.

Chance and Evolution

There is a particularly interesting interplay of chance and causality in the evolution of biological organisms. According to Darwin's theory of evolution, three influences cooperate in the process which gradually changes a species over the centuries. The first is variation, which produces slight differences in the organs of members of the same species. The second is natural selection, which picks out for preservation those members of the species whose organs give them some advantage in the struggle for existence. The third is heredity, which passes on to the next generation the characteristics of these organs that gave their owners this advantage. The major influence in the production of significant variation is now thought to be *mutation*, the sudden appearance of alterations in the genes of the germ cells. Most mutations are attributed to chance events, such as the accidental collision of cosmic rays with genes. So chance provides the raw material on which natural selection operates. But natural selection operates largely through inexorable causal laws: the strong eat the weak; the fast catch the slow, or the fast escape from the slow; and so on. As a result, although individual variations are accidental and undirected, the accumulated variations that are preserved by natural selection are directed towards better and better adaptation of the organism to the environment. Chance and causality have combined to produce the remarkable examples of functional perfection that we see in the biological world. The best example of this functional perfection is the human brain, which makes up for man's physical weakness by the power of the ideas that it creates. Probability theory is one of these powerful ideas with which man is better able to contend with his environment.

Bibliography

For readers who wish to undertake a systematic study of probability theory:

Elementary texts:

Probability, An Introduction, by Samuel Goldberg, Prentice-Hall, New York, N. Y.

Probability and Statistics, by Mosteller, Rourke and Thomas, Addison-Wesley Publishing Co., Reading, Mass.

Advanced texts:

An Introduction to Probability Theory and Its Applications, by William Feller, John Wiley & Sons, New York, N. Y.

Mathematical Methods of Statistics, by Harold Cramér, Princeton University Press, Princeton, N. J.

Theory of Probability, by M. E. Munroe, McGraw-Hill Book Co., New York, N. Y.

History:

A History of the Mathematical Theory of Probability, by I. Todhunter, Chelsea Publishing Co., New York, N. Y.

On Causality and Chance:

Causality and Chance in Modern Physics, by David Bohm, D. Van Nostrand Co., Princeton, N. J.

Answers to Exercises

Answers to Chapter I

Pascal's solution to the Problem of Points, quoted from Todhunter, *A History of the Mathematical Theory of Probability*: Suppose that the first player has gained two points and the second player one point; they have now to play for a point on this condition, that if the first player gains he takes all the money which is at stake, namely 64 pistoles, and if the second player gains each player has two points, so that they are on terms of equality, and if they leave off playing each ought to take 32 pistoles. Thus, if the first player gains, 64 pistoles belong to him, and if he loses, 32 pistoles belong to him. If, then, the players do not wish to play this game, but to separate without playing it, the first player would say to the second, "I am certain of 32 pistoles even if I lose this game, and as for the other 32 pistoles perhaps I shall have them and perhaps you will have them; the chances are equal. Let us then divide these 32 pistoles equally and give me also the 32 pistoles of which I am certain." Thus the first player will have 48 pistoles and the second 16 pistoles.

Next, suppose that the first player has gained two points and the second player none, and that they are about to play for a point; the condition then is that if the first player gains this point he secures the game and takes the 64 pistoles, and if the second player gains this point the players will then be in the situation already examined, in which the first player is entitled to 48 pistoles, and the second to 16 pistoles. Thus if they do not wish to play, the first player would say to the second, "If I gain the point I gain 64 pistoles; If I lose it I am entitled to 48 pistoles. Give me then the 48 pistoles of which I am certain, and divide the other 16 equally, since our chances of gaining the point are equal." Thus the first player will have 56 pistoles and the second player 8 pistoles.

Finally, suppose that the first player has gained one point and the second player none. If they proceed to play for a point the condition is that if the first player gains it the players will be in the situation just examined in which the first player is entitled to 56 pistoles; if the first player loses the point each player has then a point, and each is entitled to 32 pistoles. Thus if they do not wish to play, the first player would say to the second, "Give me the 32 pistoles of which I am certain and divide the remainder of the 56 pistoles equally, that is, divide 24 pistoles equally." Thus the first player will have the sum of 32 and 12 pistoles, that is 44 pistoles, and consequently the second will have 20 pistoles.

Answers to Chapter II

1. $\{a, b, c\}$, $\{a, b\}$, $\{a, c\}$, $\{b, c\}$, $\{a\}$, $\{b\}$, $\{c\}$, $\{\ \}$. The simple events are $\{a\}$, $\{b\}$, $\{c\}$. The certain event is $S = \{a, b, c\}$. The impossible event is $\varnothing = \{\ \}$. **2.** $\{x, y, z, w\}$, $\{x, y, z\}$, $\{x, y, w\}$, $\{x, z, w\}$, $\{y, z, w\}$, $\{x, y\}$, $\{x, z\}$, $\{x, w\}$, $\{y, z\}$, $\{y, w\}$, $\{z, w\}$, $\{x\}$, $\{y\}$, $\{z\}$, $\{w\}$, $\{\ \}$. **3.** 8; 16; 2^r. **4.** $E \cup F = \{0, 1, 2, 3, 4\}$; $E \cap F = \{1, 2\}$. **5.** $\{1, 2, 4, 5\}$.
6.

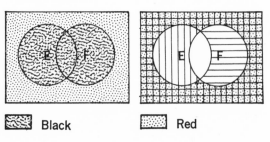

Black   Red

7.

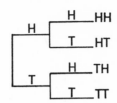

8.

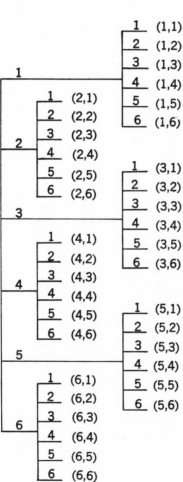

9. *HHHH, THHH, HTHH, HHTH, HHHT, TTHH, THTH, THHT, HTTH, HTHT, HHTT, TTTH, TTHT, THTT, HTTT, TTTT.* **10.** 64.

Answers to Chapter III

1. See Chapter II, exercise 9, for sample space. $E_0 = \{TTTT\}$. $E_1 = \{HTTT, THTT, TTHT, TTTH\}$. $E_2 = \{TTHH, THTH, THHT, HTTH, HTHT, HHTT\}$. $E_3 = \{THHH, HTHH, HHTH, HHHT\}$. $E_4 = \{HHHH\}$. $n(E_0) = 1$; $n(E_1) = 4$; $n(E_2) = 6$; $n(E_3) = 4$; $n(E_4) = 1$. $P(E_0) = \frac{1}{16}$; $P(E_1) = \frac{4}{16}$; $P(E_2) = \frac{6}{16}$; $P(E_3) = \frac{4}{16}$; $P(E_4) = \frac{1}{16}$. **2.** $S = \{w, r\}$; $P(\{w\}) = \frac{1}{3}$; $P(\{r\}) = \frac{2}{3}$; 1:2. **3.** $S = \{w, b, r\}$; $P(\{w\}) = \frac{2}{9}$; $P(\{b\}) = \frac{3}{9}$; $P(\{r\}) = \frac{4}{9}$; $P(\{w, b\}) = \frac{5}{9}$. **4.** $\{\{w_1, w_2, w_3\}, \{w_1, w_2, b_1\}, \{w_1, w_2, b_2\}, \{w_1, w_3, b_1\}, \{w_1, w_3, b_2\}, \{w_2, w_3, b_1\}, \{w_2, w_3, b_2\}, \{w_1, b_1, b_2\}, \{w_2, b_1, b_2\}, \{w_3, b_1, b_2\}\}$. Probability of each simple event is .1. $P(E_1) = .3$; $P(E_2) = .6$; $P(E_3) = .1$. **5.** See Chapter II, exercise 8, for sample space. Probability of each simple event is $\frac{1}{36}$. $E_2 = \{(1, 1)\}$; $E_3 = \{(1, 2), (2, 1)\}$; $E_4 = \{(1, 3), (2, 2), (3, 1)\}$; $E_5 = \{(1, 4), (2, 3), (3, 2), (4, 1)\}$; $E_6 = \{(1, 5), (2, 4), (3, 3), (4, 2), (5, 1)\}$. $E_7 = \{(1, 6), (2, 5), (3, 4), (4, 3), (5, 2), (6, 1)\}$. $P(E_2) = \frac{1}{36}$; $P(E_3) = \frac{2}{36}$; $P(E_4) = \frac{3}{36}$; $P(E_5) = \frac{4}{36}$; $P(E_6) = \frac{5}{63}$; $P(E_7) = \frac{6}{36}$. **6.** $\frac{1}{52}$; $\frac{1}{13}$; $\frac{1}{4}$; $\frac{2}{13}$. **7.** Maxwell-Boltzmann: $P(| ** | | | |) = P(| | ** | | |) = P(| | | ** | |) = P(| | | | ** |) = \frac{1}{16}$; $P(| * | * | | |) = P(| * | | * | |) = P(| * | | | * |) = P(| | * | * | |) = P(| | * | | * |) = P(| | | * | * |) = \frac{2}{16}$. Bose-Einstein: Same sample space of 10 elements. Probability of each simple event is $\frac{1}{10}$. Fermi-Dirac: Sample space contains only the last 6 elements shown in Maxwell-Boltzmann case. Probability of each simple event is $\frac{1}{6}$. **8.** 5. **9.** $(r + t)/(r + s + t) > r/(r + s)$ if and only if $(r + s)(r + t) > r(r + s + t)$ if and only if $r^2 + rs + rt + st > r^2 + rs + rt$ if and only if $st > 0$.

Answers to Chapter IV

1. 20; 120; 120. **2.** 720. **3.** 6.5530, not as accurate as the value 6.5598 shown in the table. **4.** 56, 56. **5.** 210. **6.** 5.4×10^{28}. **7.** $\frac{20}{64}$; $\frac{42}{64}$. **8.** $\frac{3}{7}$. **9.** $7!/7^7 = .006$. **10.** $\frac{12}{81}$; $\frac{1}{15}$.

11. | **** | | |, | | **** | | |, | | | **** |, | *** | * | |, | *** | | * |,
| * | *** | |, | | *** | * |, | * | | *** |, | | * | *** |, | ** | ** | |,
| ** | | ** |, | | ** | ** |, | ** | * | * |, | * | ** | * |, | * | * | ** |.

12. $\binom{1200}{3} \Big/ \binom{48000}{3}$ = approximately $\dfrac{1}{64000}$. **13.** $1 +$ $5 + 10 + 10 + 5 + 1 = 32$. **14.** 1, 5, 10, 10, 5, 1. **15.** $\frac{1}{10}$.

16. $\left[\binom{13}{2} \times 2! \times \binom{4}{3} \times \binom{4}{2} \right] \Big/ \binom{52}{5} = .07$.

17. $\binom{5}{1} \Big/ \binom{6}{2} = \frac{1}{3}$.

Answers to Chapter V

1. $\frac{11}{36}$. **2.** $\frac{21}{30}$. **3.** $\frac{16}{52}$. **4.** $\frac{21}{32}$. **5.** $\frac{721}{3375}$. **6.** .75. **7.** $P(H \mid B) = \frac{4}{12}$; $P(B \mid H) = \frac{4}{13}$. **8.** $\frac{2}{3}$. **9.** $\frac{75}{315}$, $\frac{80}{315}$, $\frac{90}{315}$, $\frac{70}{315}$. **10.** 5.7%.
11. $P(E) = P(E \cap F') + P(E \cap F)$, so $P(E \cap F') = P(E) - P(E \cap F) = P(E) - P(E)P(F) = P(E)(1 - P(F)) = P(E)P(F')$. **12.** No.
13.

Answers to Chapter VI

1.

Outcome	HHH	HHT	HTH	THH	HTT	THT	TTH	TTT
x	3	2	2	2	1	1	1	0

x	$X = x$	$P(X = x)$
0	$\{TTT\}$	$\frac{1}{8}$
1	$\{HTT, THT, TTH\}$	$\frac{3}{8}$
2	$\{HHT, HTH, THH\}$	$\frac{3}{8}$
3	$\{HHH\}$	$\frac{1}{8}$

x	0	1	2	3
$P(X = x)$	$\frac{1}{8}$	$\frac{3}{8}$	$\frac{3}{8}$	$\frac{1}{8}$

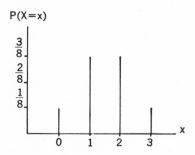

2.

x	28	30	31
$P(X = x)$	$\frac{1}{12}$	$\frac{4}{12}$	$\frac{7}{12}$

3. 1. **5.** 4. $\frac{365}{12}$.

5.

x	0	1	2	3	4
$P(X = x)$	$\frac{9}{24}$	$\frac{8}{24}$	$\frac{6}{24}$	0	$\frac{1}{24}$

$E(X) = 1.$

6. -2. **7.** 11. **8.** 0; 144. **9.** $E(W^2) = 5192.2$; $[E(W)]^2 = 5184.0$; Var $(W) = 8.2$; $\sigma_W = \sqrt{8.2}$. **10.** .866. **11.** 1. **12.** 2.4; 1.7. **13.** $X^* = (X - 2)/1$; $Y^* = (Y - 7)/2.4$; $Z^* = (Z - 3.5)/1.7$.

Answers to Chapter VII

1. a) $\{THH, HTT\}$; $\frac{2}{8}$. b) $\{HHT, HTH, THH\}$; $\frac{3}{8}$.
   c) $\{THH\}$; $\frac{1}{8}$. d) $\{HHT, HTH, THH\}$; $\frac{3}{8}$.
   e) $\{HHT, HTH, THH\}$; $\frac{3}{8}$. f) $\varnothing$; 0.
   g) $\{HHH, HHT, HTH, HTT\}$; $\frac{4}{8}$.
   h) $\{HTH, HTT, TTH, TTT\}$; $\frac{4}{8}$. i) $\{HTH, HTT\}$; $\frac{2}{8}$.

2.

X \ Z	0	1	2	3	$P(X = x)$
0	0	0	0	$\frac{1}{8}$	$\frac{1}{8}$
1	0	0	$\frac{1}{8}$	0	$\frac{1}{8}$
2	0	0	$\frac{1}{8}$	0	$\frac{1}{8}$
3	0	$\frac{1}{8}$	$\frac{1}{8}$	0	$\frac{2}{8}$
4	0	$\frac{1}{8}$	0	0	$\frac{1}{8}$
5	0	$\frac{1}{8}$	0	0	$\frac{1}{8}$
6	$\frac{1}{8}$	0	0	0	$\frac{1}{8}$
$P(Z = z)$	$\frac{1}{8}$	$\frac{3}{8}$	$\frac{3}{8}$	$\frac{1}{8}$	1

$\rho(X, Z) = -.93.$

3.

X \ U	0	1	$P(X = x)$
0	$\frac{1}{8}$	0	$\frac{1}{8}$
1	$\frac{1}{8}$	0	$\frac{1}{8}$
2	$\frac{1}{8}$	0	$\frac{1}{8}$
3	$\frac{1}{8}$	$\frac{1}{8}$	$\frac{2}{8}$
4	0	$\frac{1}{8}$	$\frac{1}{8}$
5	0	$\frac{1}{8}$	$\frac{1}{8}$
6	0	$\frac{1}{8}$	$\frac{1}{8}$
$P(U = u)$	$\frac{4}{8}$	$\frac{4}{8}$	1

$\rho(X, U) = .8.$

4.

X \ Y	-2	-1	0	1	2	$P(X = x)$
0	$\frac{1}{80}$	$\frac{2}{80}$	$\frac{1}{80}$	$\frac{3}{80}$	$\frac{3}{80}$	$\frac{1}{8}$
1	$\frac{2}{80}$	$\frac{4}{80}$	$\frac{2}{80}$	$\frac{6}{80}$	$\frac{6}{80}$	$\frac{2}{8}$
2	$\frac{3}{80}$	$\frac{6}{80}$	$\frac{3}{80}$	$\frac{9}{80}$	$\frac{9}{80}$	$\frac{3}{8}$
3	$\frac{2}{80}$	$\frac{4}{80}$	$\frac{2}{80}$	$\frac{6}{80}$	$\frac{6}{80}$	$\frac{2}{8}$
$P(Y = y)$	$\frac{1}{10}$	$\frac{2}{10}$	$\frac{1}{10}$	$\frac{3}{10}$	$\frac{3}{10}$	1

5.

$2x$	0	2	4	6
$P(2X = m)$	$\frac{1}{8}$	$\frac{2}{8}$	$\frac{3}{8}$	$\frac{2}{8}$

y^2	0	1	4
$P(Y^2 = n)$	$\frac{1}{10}$	$\frac{5}{10}$	$\frac{4}{10}$

$2X$ \\ Y^2	0	1	4	$P(2X = m)$
0	$\frac{1}{80}$	$\frac{5}{80}$	$\frac{4}{80}$	$\frac{1}{8}$
2	$\frac{2}{80}$	$\frac{10}{80}$	$\frac{8}{80}$	$\frac{2}{8}$
4	$\frac{3}{80}$	$\frac{15}{80}$	$\frac{12}{80}$	$\frac{3}{8}$
6	$\frac{2}{80}$	$\frac{10}{80}$	$\frac{8}{80}$	$\frac{2}{8}$
$P(Y^2 = n)$	$\frac{1}{10}$	$\frac{5}{10}$	$\frac{4}{10}$	1

$$P(2X = m, Y^2 = n) = P(2X = m)P(Y^2 = n).$$

6. $P(U = 0) = P(U = 1) = P(V = 0) = P(V = 1) = P(W = 0) = P(W = 1) = \frac{1}{2}. P(U = u, V = v, W = w) = \frac{1}{8}$, for $u, v, w = 0, 1$.

7.
$$\begin{aligned}
\text{Var } (X - Y) &= E([(X - Y) - E(X - Y)]^2) \\
&= E([X - Y - E(X) + E(Y)]^2) \\
&= E([(X - E(X)) - (Y - E(Y))]^2) \\
&= E((X - E(X))^2) + E((Y - E(Y))^2) \\
&\quad -2E([X - E(X)][Y - E(Y)]) \\
&= \text{Var } (X) + \text{Var } (Y) - 2 \text{ Cov } (X, Y).
\end{aligned}$$

Then $\text{Var } (X^* - Y^*) = \text{Var } (X^*) + \text{Var } (Y^*) - 2 \text{ Cov } (X^*, Y^*) = 2 - 2\rho(X, Y).$

8. If $\rho(X, Y) = -1, \text{Var } (X^* + Y^*) = 2(1 + \rho(X, Y)) =$

0. Then for possible values, $X^* + Y^* = E(X^* + Y^*) =$

0, and $X^* = -Y^*$. Then $\dfrac{X - \mu_X}{\sigma_X} = -\dfrac{Y - \mu_Y}{\sigma_Y}$, and $Y =$

$-\left(\dfrac{\sigma_Y}{\sigma_X}\right)X + \dfrac{\sigma_Y\mu_X + \sigma_X\mu_Y}{\sigma_X}.$

9.

Y \ Z	0	1	2	3	$P(Y = y)$
0	0	0	0	$\frac{1}{8}$	$\frac{1}{8}$
1	0	0	$\frac{3}{8}$	0	$\frac{3}{8}$
2	0	$\frac{3}{8}$	0	0	$\frac{3}{8}$
3	$\frac{1}{8}$	0	0	0	$\frac{1}{8}$
$P(Z = z)$	$\frac{1}{8}$	$\frac{3}{8}$	$\frac{3}{8}$	$\frac{1}{8}$	1

$\rho(Y, Z) = (E(YZ) - E(Y)E(Z))/\sigma_Y\sigma_Z =$
$(1.5 - (1.5)(1.5))/\sqrt{.75}\sqrt{.75} = -1.$

10.

X \ Y	1	4	$P(X = x)$
-2	0	$\frac{1}{4}$	$\frac{1}{4}$
-1	$\frac{1}{4}$	0	$\frac{1}{4}$
1	$\frac{1}{4}$	0	$\frac{1}{4}$
2	0	$\frac{1}{4}$	$\frac{1}{4}$
$P(Y = y)$	$\frac{2}{4}$	$\frac{2}{4}$	1

$E(XY) = 0.$
$E(X) = 0.$
$E(Y) = 0.$
Therefore
Cov $(X, Y) = 0,$
and $\rho(X, Y) = 0.$

11. $\rho(M, F) = .53$.

Answers to Chapter VIII

1. a)

(x_1, x_2, x_3)	Probability	$\bar{x}$
$(1, 1, 1)$	.027	$\frac{3}{3}$
$(1, 1, 2)$	.054	$\frac{4}{3}$
$(1, 1, 3)$	.009	$\frac{5}{3}$

and so on. There are 27 possible values of (X_1, X_2, X_3)

b)

$\bar{x}$	$\frac{3}{3}$	$\frac{4}{3}$	$\frac{5}{3}$	$\frac{6}{3}$	$\frac{7}{3}$	$\frac{8}{3}$	$\frac{9}{3}$
$P(\bar{X} = \bar{x})$	.027	.162	.351	.324	.117	.018	.001

$E(X) = 1.8. \ E(\bar{X}) = 1.8. \ \sigma_X = .60. \ \sigma_{\bar{X}} = .35.$

c)

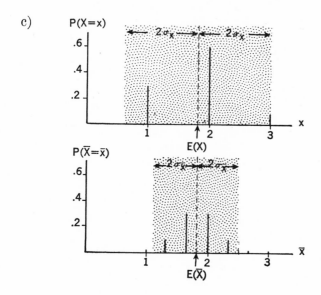

2. 100. **3.** At least 90%. **4.** a) .2. b) .1896.

Answers to Chapter IX

1. .401; .086; .315. **2.** .738. **3.** .874. **4.** 100; $10\sqrt{6}/3$.
5. .780. **6.** .9; 900.

Answers to Chapter X

1. .4332; .8664; .9270.
2. $E(X) = 3$. $\sigma_X = 1.22$.

x	−0.5	0.5	1.5	2.5	3.5	4.5	5.5	6.5
$x*$	−2.9	−2.0	−1.2	−0.4	0.4	1.2	2.0	2.9

r	−2.9	−2.0	−1.2	−0.4	0.4	1.2	2.0	2.9
$P(X* \geqq r)$	1	.984	.891	.656	.344	.109	0.16	0
$P(N* \geqq r)$	.9981	.9972	.8849	.6554	.3446	.1151	.0228	.0019

3. 6.7%; 4.4%; 15.9%.

Answers to Chapter XI

1. .04. **2.** $b(2; 10, .1) = .174$. $p(2; 1) = .184$.

Index